KERCHING!

Paul Manship

Gomer

First published in 2019 by Gomer Press,
Llandysul, Ceredigion SA44 4JL

ISBN 978 1 78562 303 5

A CIP record for this title is available from the British Library.

This book is published with the financial support of the
Welsh Books Council.

Printed and bound in Wales at
Gomer Press, Llandysul, Ceredigion
www.gomer.co.uk

CHAPTER ONE

Birthday Fun

I virtually ran down the stairs. Today was the big day! The day I'd finally get my PS4. Most of my classmates already had one, but today it was my turn.

A big, shiny *HAPPY BIRTHDAY* banner was draped over the fireplace and, in front of the TV, lay a small pile of envelopes and three wrapped presents, one clearly a DVD. Mum kissed me on the cheek and wished me happy birthday. Dad had already left for work.

I greedily ripped open the envelopes, skimmed through the messages from my relatives, then counted out the money.

One of the three presents looked just about the right size to make this the best day ever.

The DVD was from Danielle, my sister. It was *Fast*

and Furious 7, which is not a bad film. However, I knew she'd only paid £3 for it in Asda.

Mum looked on with a pained expression while I opened the other two presents, which were from her and Dad.

I ripped off the wrapping paper. I couldn't believe what I was looking at. They'd gone and bought me a board game – Monopoly – and a boxed set of Roald Dahl books.

No PS4 in sight.

'Thanks, Mum,' I said, faking a smile.

She could tell I wasn't happy. 'Don't you like them?'

'They're okay,' I said.

'But I thought you said you liked Monopoly when we played it with your cousins last Christmas.'

I put my shoes on ready for school.

'Well?'

'I like giraffes,' I muttered, 'but that doesn't mean I want one.'

'What's wrong with board games?' said Mum, obviously upset. 'I had loads of them when I was your age.'

'That was then.'

'Hey! Anyway, I've got the receipts. You can take everything back and get something else if you like.'

I found the receipts in one of the kitchen drawers. The game was £16.99 and the books were £39.99.

Mum caught me looking at them. 'I wish you'd be more grateful,' she said.

'I am grateful, but aren't birthdays supposed to be special?'

Granddad sauntered in, in his dressing gown. He'd obviously overheard the last part of the conversation. 'When I was a boy, all I used to have in my Christmas stocking was an apple, an orange and a book.'

'But that was in prehistoric times,' I snapped, pulling my coat on.

'Don't talk to your granddad like that!' Mum yelled.

I pushed my way through the door and headed off to school.

Happy birthday to me.

* * *

Owen barged into me as I hung up my coat outside our classroom.

'Have you done that homework Miss set us?' he asked me.

It hadn't really been proper homework. We'd been asked to interview members of our families and find out what they thought about money.

For me, money is pretty straightforward – you've either got it or you haven't. My family – that's me, Mum, Dad, Danielle and Granddad – definitely haven't.

To be honest, I find it a bit irritating that my name is Rich – short for Richie or Richard. My family is definitely *not* rich. As far as I can see, apart from homeless people and starving children in Africa, everyone has more money than us.

Owen wanted to know what I'd had for my birthday, but I wouldn't tell him. It was just too embarrassing. He tried to cheer me up with some jokes, but they didn't work.

After sorting out the registers, Mrs Lloyd was straight on it. 'I must say, I'm really keen to see what your families think.'

Riley Jones had his hand straight in the air, waving it around like an excited windsock. He always has his hand in the air, as if he has no control over it. One day it's going to detach itself and fly off.

'I asked my nan, Miss,' he said, enthusiastically.

'And?'

'And she said that money never makes anyone happy and the more you have, the more you want.'

I shook my head in disgust. It would be nice to have the chance to find out what it's like to *have* money and then at least I could see whether it made me happy or not.

My dad is always saying, *Don't worry, kiddo, next week we're gonna win the lottery.* I googled the UK lottery once and found out that, basically, you have a one in fourteen million chance of winning. You've got more chance of a pink elephant in silk pyjamas knocking on your front door. I shared this fact with my dad, who shrugged and said, 'Well, somebody's got to win it.'

'I think I know what your nan means, Riley,' said Mrs Lloyd, nodding wisely. 'Some people think that money is the root of all evil.'

I must have been scowling because Miss honed in on me. 'You look like you don't agree, Richie.'

I went a bit red. 'Uh, well, having no money can

cause problems too,' I said. You don't have to watch *The Jeremy Kyle Show* or *EastEnders* to know that.

'True, true,' she said.

Raj chirped in, 'My dad says that money makes the world go round.'

He would say that. His dad has his own furniture business. His family has got money coming out of its ears.

Owen made some jazz hands and started singing, *'Money, money money, must be funny ... in a rich man's world.'*

In my opinion, the opposite is definitely true. Having no money is not funny at all.

Owen nudged me. 'If I was rich, Rich, I'd be laughing my head off. Ha ha ha bonk.'

I pulled a face at him. 'Ha ha ha bonk?'

'Yeah, that's the sound of my head falling off.'

Mrs Lloyd sat on the end of our desk. 'Has anyone ever heard this expression, *A fool and his money are soon parted*?'

My family had had first-hand experience of this. Two years ago, one of my nans died, leaving my mum and dad £1,000 in her will. Dad bought a car and, two weeks later, he had to sell it for scrap because the head gasket had blown. The guy he'd bought it from said that he couldn't understand it – as far as he was concerned, the car was okay. It had passed its MOT and had a recent service. Anyway, basically £1,000 went swishing down the drain.

'My father says that money talks,' said Raj.

Owen broke into song again: '*I need a dollar, a dollar is what I need.*'

Ignoring him, Mrs Lloyd wrote a sentence on her whiteboard: *There are people who have money and there are people who are rich.* 'What do you think about that, then?' she said.

Mrs Lloyd is really keen on philosophy. She's always asking us 'big questions', even though we're only ten and eleven. She said she likes to have a dialogic classroom, whatever that means.

The sentence didn't make sense at all to me. If you haven't got any money, how can you possibly be rich?

'What do you think, Richie?' she said. Today was obviously pick-on-Richie day.

'Uh … does it mean that there are people who have money and there are other people who have things, like cars, clothes, houses and jewellery, because they've spent all their money?'

Mrs Lloyd half-frowned, half-smiled. 'Well, I'm not sure that's what the person who wrote it meant.'

'Who did write it?' Raj asked.

Mrs Lloyd made her way to another part of the class. 'Actually, to be honest, I don't know.'

I muttered to Owen, under my breath, 'Well how can she know what the person meant, then?'

I thought for a second Miss had heard me. Thankfully, she hadn't. 'So,' she asked the class, 'can you be rich if you've got no money?'

What a stupid question!

Andrea spoke up. 'If you are happy and you have a family that loves you, you can be rich.' This is typical of her. She's a Christian and goes to church every week, and Sunday School too. Owen and I quite like her, even though she's sort of a Miss Goody Two-Shoes. She hangs around with us quite a lot.

'Can money buy you love?' Miss asked us.

'Money can buy *anything*,' I said with confidence.

'You shouldn't love somebody for their money, though,' said Andrea.

This whole discussion was getting on my nerves. Nobody can deny that having money makes life a lot easier and I still wished my family had a load more of it.

Completely randomly, Owen shouted out, 'It's Richie's birthday today.'

I planted a kick on his shin under the table.

'Of course it is,' smiled Mrs Lloyd. 'I forgot. Come up here, Rich. Everybody put down your pens. Let's sing happy birthday to this lovely young man.'

So I had to stand there, red-faced, through a very badly sung version of *'Penblwydd Hapus'*. Why do teachers feel the need to do this? It's absolute torture.

'Aren't you supposed to bring in a cake if it's your birthday?' Riley declared.

Most pupils bring in huge, rectangular slabs from Tesco's or Asda, large enough so that twenty-five kids can have a slice each. When it was her birthday, Andrea brought in individual cupcakes, with characters from *Alice in Wonderland* on them. A few months ago, Raj bought in not one, but two cakes from Marks & Spencer's: a triple-layered carrot cake and something called an Extremely Chocolatey Party Cake. I ate so much I was nearly sick.

I'd meant to ask my mum to buy me a cake on the weekend but I'd forgotten.

'Okay,' said Mrs Lloyd, winding things up, 'that was a very interesting start to our mini-topic. We're going to spend the next three weeks looking at money …'

Wonderful!

'As well as doing lots of work in the classroom, I'd like to give you all an assignment to do at home. Basically, you can do whatever you like – a PowerPoint, a story, some research, graphs – as long as it's got something to do with money. In three weeks' time, you can show us what you've come up with.'

I didn't feel inspired at all. And I didn't have the tiniest clue what to do.

* * *

On the yard, Owen started bouncing around like Tigger. I don't know where he gets his energy. He hardly seems to eat anything. His is one of the few families in our school worse off than mine. He has five brothers.

'What are you gonna do?' he said. 'For the project thingy?'

I shrugged.

'Well I know what *I'm* gonna do,' he virtually

yelled in my ear. 'I'm gonna collect as many jokes as I can about money and then do a stand-up routine.'

Owen's dream is to be a comedian when he grows up. Unfortunately, Owen isn't always as funny as he thinks he is.

'*You'd* better think of something,' he said. 'Why don't you find out what money they use in different countries, like dollars or rupees or yen?'

I didn't answer him.

'What's up with you?' he asked me. 'Why are you so grumpy today? You should be happy. It's your birthday.'

Raj jogged past us.

'Hey Rajji,' Owen called out. 'What are you planning to do?'

'Football.' He pointed at his brand new trainers.

'Not *now*,' Owen laughed. 'For the homework?'

'Oh, that. I'm going to set up a mini-enterprise.'

Greedy so-and-so, I thought. As if he hasn't got enough money already. He had a PS4 the day they came out. Raj always has the best of everything.

Owen scratched his head. 'A mini-what?'

'He's gonna sell stuff and make money,' I explained.

'What kind of stuff?'

'Who knows?'

Owen's face was a picture of confusion. 'I didn't know kids could have their own businesses.'

'They can if they're greedy,' I said.

* * *

Six hours later, I was sitting on the sofa in our living room with a tray on my lap, eating a microwave lasagna from Aldi's. Mum and Dad were watching *Crimewatch*.

We'd just watched this weird programme where these little kids had to sit in front of a Smartie on a saucer for five minutes without eating it. If they managed to succeed, they got two Smarties. They all failed miserably.

I hadn't given the homework any further thought. We had three whole weeks to do it. I'd think of something, eventually. I just couldn't drum up any enthusiasm at that moment.

I heard the front door open: my sister, Danielle. She called out from the hallway, 'Mum, can I have some money for my driving lesson?'

Mum stopped chewing momentarily. 'There's

twenty pounds in the mug in the kitchen cupboard. I want change, mind.'

Dad's knife and fork froze, mid-air. He glanced at my mum. 'I thought we agreed she could pay for her own lessons, as she's working.'

Mum had a pained expression on her face. 'But, babes, she's trying to save for a car. She's got £500 already.'

My ears pricked up. 'Five hundred pounds?' I gasped. 'How much does she get paid?'

'About six pounds an hour,' said Mum. Danielle works Saturdays and Sundays in Hush Puppies in Cardiff.

I tried to work out how much she earned a week. I knew she worked 10am-5pm on Saturday and 11am-4pm on Sunday. It was definitely enough for her to be able to help out paying for her driving lessons.

Dad shook his head. 'I hope she knows she'll have to pay for insurance. There goes another thousand pounds.'

I'm not really sure what insurance is, but whatever it is, it should be good at that price.

'Don't be so negative all the time, luv,' Mum told him.

'I'm not being negative, I'm being realistic.'

'With you, the cup's always half-empty.'

I had no idea how the conversation had switched to cups. I followed Mum out to the kitchen to help her with the washing-up.

'Mu-um?' I said.

'What?'

Dad called out from the living room, 'Tell him no, whatever it is.'

'Be quiet, grumpy-guts,' she called back at him. She nudged me. 'What is it, Rich?'

'As it's my birthday, can I invite my friends to the cinema and McDonald's on the weekend?'

She pursed her lips. 'How many friends?'

I did a quick count. 'Four?'

Dad called out, 'As long as they all pay for themselves.'

Mum pulled a face. 'Ignore him,' she said. 'He's just being silly.'

Dad appeared in the kitchen. 'I'm not being silly. We can't afford it. You're talking £5 each for

McDonald's and £6 each for the cinema, and that's without popcorn. We're not made of money, y'know.'

Outside the kitchen window, Danielle was attempting to drive off in the instructor's car. She'd already stalled twice.

I took a deep breath. 'But you just gave *her* £20.'

'That's different.'

'Well, what *can* I do for my birthday, then?'

Mum pondered. 'You can ask a few of your friends to sleep over on Saturday, if you like. Maybe Owen and one other. I'll get some pizzas from Asda.'

Dad raised his eyebrows. He walked off, muttering under his breath, 'We never had sleepovers in my day.'

I stacked some plates. 'Did they have beds?'

'Don't be cheeky,' Mum smirked.

I took a deep breath. 'Mum,' I said, 'do you think I can have a PS4 for Christmas?'

A plate slipped from her hand and fell to the floor.

Dad came rushing back into the kitchen. Miraculously, the plate spun around for a bit, then settled, without breaking.

'Tell me I didn't just hear him say PS4,' he said.

I turned away.

'Do you realise how much those things cost?'

'No idea,' I said. 'A hundred quid?'

He laughed. 'And the rest. You're talking over three hundred pounds.' He scraped his plate clean and virtually threw it into the washing-up bowl.

Outside, Danielle stalled again.

Dad tutted. 'How many blinking lessons has she had? She shouldn't still be doing that.'

I tried a last-minute ploy. 'All my friends have got one.' This wasn't exactly 100% true. However, quite a few of them *did* or were going to get one.

'Conversation over,' Dad said, heading back into the living room and closing the door behind him.

My reflection stared back at me from the kitchen window. It was not a happy face. I abandoned my post at the sink and made for the stairs.

'Hey, you haven't finished!' Mum called after me.

'Maybe I should get paid for helping out,' I called back.

* * *

I lay on my bed.

Downstairs, just below my bedroom, Mum and Dad began a heated conversation. Their voices were muffled so I couldn't hear exactly what they were saying, but I knew it was about me.

Not long after, there was a gentle tap on my door. Mum came in and sat on my bed.

'I don't wanna talk,' I said.

She looked upset. 'Don't be like that. Me and your father have been having a bit of a chat and we've agreed that you help out quite a lot around the house for your age. If you keep doing your little jobs, we'll give you a weekly allowance.'

'A what?'

'Money.'

I sat up. 'How much?'

'Five pounds a week.'

I lay back down again. 'A fiver?' I knew for a fact that Raj got fifteen pounds a week, and that was *without* doing any chores.

My mum sighed. 'That's all we can afford, Richie. Your dad and I don't get paid a lot.'

That's another thing that bugs me. The fact that my mum and dad don't seem to earn as much as other people. Aren't they as clever as other people?

Mum patted my leg. 'Okay?'

'When does it start?' I said.

'How about this Saturday?'

After she'd gone, I quickly worked out how may fives there are in three hundred. Sixty. Sixty weeks! It would take me over a year to save enough money to buy a PS4. I slumped back on my bed.

£ CHAPTER TWO £

Money Money Money

In class, it soon became obvious that Mrs Lloyd was going to try and find every single opportunity to link things in with money.

'In our numeracy lesson today,' she said, 'we are going to focus on doubling.'

Owen looked confused. 'Isn't that in Ireland?'

Miss raised her eyebrows. 'Not Dublin, you doughnut. Doubling.' Mrs Lloyd quite often refers to people as doughnuts. I'm not sure if she's supposed to. Most of the kids in the class find it amusing. Of course, it's not so much fun if it's *you* who's being called the doughnut.

'I know how to double your money, Miss,' said Owen. Once he starts, he never lets up.

Mrs Lloyd surrendered. 'How?'

'You hold it up in front of the mirror. Get it?'

Reluctantly, Miss smiled. 'Not bad, Owen. Anyway, today we are going to carry out an investigation called Double Your Money. Now, if I gave you a magic penny which automatically doubles in value every day, how much do you think it would be worth in a month?'

That was a pretty difficult question. Riley looked like his brain was hurting already.

'So, tomorrow, it would become 2p,' said Raj. 'The next day it would become 4p, and so on?'

'Exactly. Any guesses?

'A hundred pounds?' offered Andrea.

Mrs Lloyd smiled and shook her head. 'A bit more than that, Andrea.'

'Ten thousand pounds?' said Raj.

'Try it in pairs. You can use a calculator if it starts to get really tricky.'

Fifteen minutes later, and with the use of a calculator, most people had worked out that the magic penny would now be worth one billion, seventy-three million, seven hundred and forty-one thousand, eight hundred and twenty-four pounds! Boy, did I want that magic penny!

* * *

Miss asked us if anybody had any ideas about what they were going to do for their money projects? 'What about you, Raj?'

'I'm going to make some money,' he said, enthusiastically.

'*Make* money?' said Owen, confused.

'Yes, I will be finding ways to earn money. I've started already. I sold lemonade on the weekend at my mum's fitness club and made ten pounds.'

I sat up straight. 'Ten pounds?'

Miss smiled and nodded. 'Very enterprising, Raj. We could be looking at the next Lord Sugar here, everybody.'

'Actually, he's one of my heroes,' Raj informed us.

Other children shared their project ideas, which ranged from explaining how money is made to writing and performing a song about money to doing some pie charts about pocket money.

One of the girls said she was going to do a mini-project on the history of money. Unfortunately, that got Miss rambling on about something called bartering. Basically, before there was actual money, people used to barter or trade with each other to pay for the things they needed, using things like animals, food, seashells and beads. Three eggs might buy a loaf of bread. Ten chickens might be enough for a pig. I wondered how many chickens I'd need for a PS4.

'I don't think bartering is a very sensible system,' said Owen.

'Why not?'

'Well, you can't exactly carry a pig around in your pocket, can you, or a bunch of chickens?'

Miss shook her head in bewilderment. '*Bunch* of chickens?'

'And,' he continued, ignoring her, 'say you wanted a loaf of bread, but you only had a cow to trade. You wouldn't want to get rid of your whole cow for a loaf of bread. And you couldn't exactly break bits off a cow to trade with.'

'Unless it's dead,' said Riley.

'Unless it's dead,' agreed Owen.

Both as daft as each other.

*   *   *

After school, Owen came back to my house. We had a sort of day-late birthday tea: sandwiches, sausage rolls, cheese and pineapple on sticks, jelly and ice cream.

He told my mum all about our homework and that he'd started collecting jokes about money.

'Sounds fun,' she said. 'How many have you got so far?'

He started counting on his fingers and then said, 'One.'

I nearly spat my Coke out.

'Where does Dracula keep his money?' he asked her.

'In the blood bank?' she said.

'Aww, you've heard it.' His face was a picture.

Granddad came in halfway through the conversation and thought we were talking about honey, not money. He said he knew a poem about honey:

I eat my peas with honey,
I've done it all my life,
It makes the peas taste funny
But it keeps them on my knife.

I'm surrounded by nutcases.

Dad shouted out from the living room. 'Where can you always find money?'

Not in this house, I thought.

'In the dictionary,' he bellowed.

Owen liked it. He now had *two* jokes.

Mum glanced at me. 'What are you gonna do for *your* homework, Rich?'

I still didn't have a clue.

*   *   *

After Owen had gone home and I'd had a bath, I sat with Dad in the living room watching telly, but he wasn't really watching it, I could tell. He had something on his mind.

'Dad?'

'Yup.'

'You said we're not exactly rolling in money. Why aren't we? You work hard. Mum works hard. How come we haven't got very much, then?'

He turned the TV down a bit. 'You're right. We do work hard but, unfortunately, not all jobs pay the same amount of money.'

'Don't you get paid very much, then?'

'Not really, no.'

I thought about it. 'But can't you get a better job?'

He paused as he lifted his mug towards his mouth. I could almost hear him counting to ten in his head.

'To get good jobs, you need qualifications.'

'Why haven't you got qualifications?' I asked him.

His head went back and he puffed out his cheeks. 'To be honest, Rich, I wasted a lot of time in school, clowning around. I was too interested in sport. I wanted to be a footballer. Your mum was brighter than I was, but she had to stay home a lot and look after *her* mum, who wasn't very well.'

I thought about all this. 'But it's not fair that some people have money and others don't.'

Dad shrugged. 'Some people are just lucky. My friend Jason, his mum and dad both died, leaving him lots of money and a house. Thankfully, my mum and dad are still alive. I certainly don't want them to die so we can have more money. Do you?'

I shook my head.

'And some people have lots of money because they're on the fiddle,' he added, bitterly.

'On the *what*? What does that mean?'

'It means that they've got jobs but they pretend

that they haven't, so they can sponge more money off the government.'

'Can't *you* do that?' I said.

He shook his head and frowned. 'If I wanted to be a criminal, I'd go and rob a bank.'

'How come Raj has loads of money?'

'Well, that's different. Raj's dad took a big risk when he decided to start up that furniture business of his. It's a gamble, though, setting up your own business. You can make loads and loads of money, but you could also end up going bankrupt.'

Dad reached for the remote and switched channels. Liverpool were playing. He'd clearly had enough of my questions.

Just in front of the telly, the Monopoly game lay on the carpet, still in its plastic wrap. I picked it up and headed to my room.

I sat on my bed and opened my present, pulling out the board and all the other stuff. I played around with the pieces for a bit – the thimble, the racing car, the boot, the battleship and the top hat. I remembered I *did* actually like playing Monopoly. Mum was right. It was just that I didn't want it for my main birthday present.

I pulled out all the money and sorted it into piles. I thought it would be fun to count it all. It came to a grand total of £15,138. I held it all together against my forehead, imagining it was real and that I'd just won it.

Acting on a strange uncontrollable impulse, I suddenly yelled, 'Woo-hoo!' and threw it all in the air. I stood, arms raised, while all the lovely cash rained down on me.

I'd made a proper mess. There was money everywhere. If I was a millionaire, I could do this with *real* money?

As I began to gather it all up, I heard shouting from below. It's quite normal for Mum and Dad to shout, so I ignored it at first. But then the volume suddenly shot up a few notches. I could hear my name mentioned and I also heard the word PS4.

Opening my bedroom door, I slowly and quietly made my way down the stairs. The raised voices continued.

I perched on the bottom step. It sounded like Mum was on my side and that she was actually trying to get me my PS4.

'Luv,' said Dad, 'I would love to be able to get it for

him, really I would. I'm not taking out a loan for it, though.'

'We could both work some extra shifts,' she pleaded.

'Are you kidding? We're both exhausted already. Richie has no idea about money. He doesn't know anything about what we earn and what we have to pay out each month.'

'Tell me, then,' I said. I couldn't help myself. It was out of my mouth before I could stop it.

Dad came around the corner, looking none too happy. 'What are you doing lurking here in the dark? Have you been listening?'

Mum joined him. 'Richie?'

I looked down at my feet. 'Your voices were really loud. I was worried.'

Dad put his arm around Mum's shoulder, pulled her towards him and planted a kiss on her cheek. 'Don't be daft. We're just having a heated discussion.'

'About me and the PS4,' I said.

They looked at each other.

'Well, yes,' Dad confessed.

'Tell him why he can't have it,' said Mum.

He scowled. 'Really?'

'Yes, really.'

Dad gathered us together in the living room and gave me a mini-lecture, all about how he takes home just over £1,000 a month as a hospital porter, about how Mum earns £150 a month working part-time behind the bar and about how, apart from spending money on food and clothes and petrol, they have to pay for something called a mortgage which will take them at least another fifteen years to pay off.

'Moor-gij?' I said. I'd never heard of it. I was wondering if, maybe, he was making it up

'It's a French word,' he said, as if that helped me understand.

I frowned. 'We owe money to French people?'

He shook his head and laughed.

'What does mortgage mean, then?'

'It means we don't own this house,' he said. 'The bank bought it for us and we're slowly paying it back.'

'But how long will it take?'

'Another fifteen years, as I said.'

'What!?!'

He then told me that, every month, they had to pay somebody for gas, electricity and water.

'But I thought water was free,' I said. I was flabbergasted.

'Well, it isn't. And nor is food.'

I knew that. I know that we spend about £70 a week on food, which isn't a lot really for five people, but Mum buys cheap brands and looks out for special offers.

'And,' Dad continued, 'don't forget, there's phone bills, birthdays and Christmas. Thankfully, me and your mum packed in smoking two years ago.'

Mum didn't look happy. Dad patted her leg. She pulled it away from him.

'Anyway, all of this means that we have to focus on what we need rather than what we want.'

I was gutted. This sounded final. No PS4 for me.

He grabbed my arm and gave it a squeeze. 'Unfortunately, Richie, people can't always get what they want. I want a Ferrari but I'm never gonna get one. However, I do need four wheels, which is why I've got that clapped-out, grey Nissan Micra sitting out there on the road.'

I felt slightly ill.

Dad ruffled my hair. 'Are you okay? You look shell-shocked. I'm not sure whether it was the right thing to explain all this to you. I hope you're big enough to understand.'

I gave my head a bit of a shake. 'Are you happy, Dad? Mum?'

'Of course we're happy,' said Dad, speaking for both of them. 'We've got our family, haven't we? Unfortunately, just when it looks like we can start making ends meet, somebody moves the goalposts.' He leant on me to get up. 'I wish we could buy you more for your birthday. I wish we could buy your sister a car. But we have to concentrate on keeping a roof over our heads, clothes on our backs and food on our plates.'

He reached into his pocket and held out two money notes. Real ones. A fiver and a tenner.

'What's that?' I said.

'Your new weekly allowance. And, as it's your birthday, there's an extra tenner.'

I hesitated, my mouth wide open.

He grabbed my hand and shoved the notes into it. 'Have it, Sunny Jim, you deserve it. You're a good boy. You make your bed every day, you help your mum with the washing up, you help me in the garden.'

'I'm gonna get a paper round,' I said, as he began to walk away.

Dad pulled a face. 'You can't, unfortunately. You're not old enough. You have to be thirteen. I appreciate the thought, though.' He came back, leaned over and kissed me on top of the head. 'Happy birthday, son.' He was all flushed and his eyes looked sore.

'Thanks, Dad.'

'We'll leave it at that, then,' he said, heading off towards the toilet.

I frowned. 'He's not crying, is he?' I said to Mum.

Her eyes were welling up too. 'It's not easy being a parent, y'know.'

I was puzzled. 'But men don't cry.'

'I think you'll find they do,' she said.

£ CHAPTER THREE £

A Penny for the SpongeBob

It was breaktime. I was sitting with Andrea in the outside hut. It was so cold we could see our breath.

'So, have you finally started your project yet?' she asked.

'Nope. Owen has, though. He's collecting money jokes. He's got two so far.'

She shook her head'

Owen spotted us and sprinted over, squeezing in between us on the bench. 'So what are you two lovebirds up to?' he said.

Andrea elbowed him in the arm.

I asked him if he had any more award-winning jokes.

He nodded. 'There was a good one on the telly last night. What did the duck say after he bought a drink in a restaurant?' Brief pause. 'Put it on my bill. Get it, get it?' He patted his nose. 'Put it on my bill.' Owen drinks way too much Red Bull.

Andrea was planning to make a PowerPoint about charity. I asked her how it was going.

'Okay,' she nodded. 'Did you know that Muslims give 2.5% of their income to charity? If everyone in the world gave 2.5%, there would be no more poverty. That's a fact.'

I didn't know that. I quickly worked out that if my family were Muslims, we would have to give away over £25 a month. That seemed like a lot – over £300 a year. Mum and Dad are pretty generous and always raise money for things like Children in Need and Red Nose Day, but I'm not sure they could afford to give away £300 a year.

Last night, maybe unsurprisingly, I'd had a dream about money. I was being chased down the street by it. Thousands and thousands of notes, all flying through the air after me, pecking at me like birds. As I whipped around a corner to get away, I came face-to-face with a huge coin rolling down the hill towards me like Indiana Jones's boulder. I woke up in a sweat.

'I wonder where money comes from,' I said.

'Out of cashpoint machines,' said Owen. 'People type in their pin numbers and, like magic, hey presto, out the money comes. Ping!'

'But where does *that* money come from?'

'It's in their bank accounts,' said Andrea.

'But where does the money in your bank account come from?'

'You put it in there,' said Owen.

We were going around in circles.

'Or somebody else does,' said Andrea. 'The people you work for. You have to earn your money. Unless you're lucky enough to win the lottery or someone leaves you money in their will.'

That sounded good to me.

'I'm gonna earn loads of money when I grow up,' I said. I certainly had no intention of being a hospital porter or working behind a bar.

'Me too,' said Owen, enthusiastically. 'I'm gonna earn loads of spondoolies. Loads of smackeroos. Loads of dosh.'

'And how are you gonna do that?' I said.

'Duh. As a world-famous comedian.'

'Oh yeah. I forgot.'

'I wonder which jobs pay the most money,' I said.

'Dunno,' said Andrea. 'Probably people like doctors, lawyers, business people, architects, engineers, computer experts.'

'Football players,' Owen added. 'Pop stars. Film stars.'

'What do you wanna be, Richie?' Andrea asked me.

I was thinking I'd like to set up my own business like Raj's dad, take a risk and make as much money as possible, so I could have a flash car, a swimming pool, a tennis court, a house with five bedrooms, designer clothes.

I'd read recently that Richard Branson is worth 4.5 billion pounds and he's the fourth richest citizen in the UK. He's a god.

'I think money is made in the Royal Mint,' said Andrea. 'That's why, if you have a lot of money, they say you are minted.'

I wondered how they worked out how much money to make in the Royal Mint. Who made *that* decision?

* * *

On the way home, I suddenly had a great idea how to make some money.

Bonfire Night was still a few weeks away but the previous weekend I'd seen some teenagers loitering outside the local Spar doing Penny for the Guy. It looked like they had quite a bit of money in their container. *I* could do that. It wasn't illegal, as far as I was aware. You didn't have to be thirteen to do it.

I texted Owen and Andrea: *Hey, you two, fancy coming around my house tomorrow morning? We could make a guy.*

They seemed keen. Owen texted back: *I've got a mask. I'll bring it.* Andrea brought some old clothes that her mum was taking to the charity shop and a sewing needle and thread. I found a pile of old newspapers in the shed.

Owen's mask wasn't exactly what we'd been expecting. It was about as far from Guy Fawkes as you could imagine. Basically, it was SpongeBob SquarePants.

'We're not using that, 'I told him.

'Why not?' he protested. 'It's gonna burn on the bonfire anyway.'

'But people won't give us money for something that looks nothing like Guy Fawkes.'

'Who's Guy Fawkes?' he actually said.

'Can you believe him?' I said to Andrea.

Owen shrugged. 'Last year, I saw one with a Bart Simpson head and the year before there was a Simon Cowell one.'

Andrea sewed the mask to the neck of an old jumper, then tied up the sleeve-ends, while Owen and I scrunched up newspaper into balls. We stuffed them into SpongeBob's upper body, while Andrea sewed tight the ends of a tatty old pair of trousers. After cramming those with newspapers too, she attached the jumper to the trousers.

It wasn't exactly the best guy in the world. It was about as fat as Augustus Gloop and had a yellow head and no feet.

Danielle walked in on us, burst out laughing, walked back out, then returned a minute later with a pink, glittery party wig.

'Cool,' said Owen, standing back and admiring our creation.

Cool it definitely wasn't. 'It doesn't look anything like Guy Fawkes, does it?' I said.

'How do you know what this Guy Fawkes fella looks like?' said Owen.

Andrea took a step back. 'I'm pretty sure he didn't look like this.'

*　　*　　*

That afternoon, we put SpongeBob into action. We found an old pushchair that someone had dumped in the lane behind my house and we dragged it along to Bettws shopping centre.

The shopping centre is basically a big square, with about twenty shops around the perimeter. There's a bakery, a DVD rental store, a fish-and-chip shop, a hairdresser's, a greetings card shop, a butcher's, a newsagent's, a grocer's, a dentist, a chemist and a small supermarket called the Spar. Also in the vicinity are the library, the police station and The Nightingale pub. Perched on top of the shops are some flats.

We parked SpongeBob outside the entrance to the Spar, right next to some trolleys.

Straight away, people started laughing and pointing. One bloke shook his head in disbelief. '*Britain's Got Talent*, is it?'

We'd forgotten to make a sign saying *Penny for the Guy*. And we'd also forgotten to bring anything to collect any money in. Owen rummaged in a bin and found an empty McDonald's Coca-Cola drinks container.

Ten minutes later, with the three of us standing there like losers, we still hadn't made any money. There was plenty of laughter but no coinage.

Owen paced back and forth. 'They're not gonna give us anything if we don't ask.'

'*I'm* not asking them,' Andrea insisted.

An old lady toddled towards us, carrying an empty canvas bag. Owen suddenly leapt in front of her, nearly giving her a heart attack.

'Oh my word,' she said, clutching her chest. 'I haven't had so much excitement for years.'

Owen pointed at SpongeBob. 'Penny for the guy?'

She glanced at our handiwork. 'Is that who it is? I thought it was my husband for a moment, after one too many.'

Owen stood his ground.

The old lady curved her way around him. 'I haven't got any change at the moment, flower. I might see you on the way back out.'

Quite a few people made that promise, only they didn't come back. They probably nipped out quickly after doing their shopping and sneaked off in the opposite direction.

A dude in biker gear came striding around the corner, helmet dangling from his hand. Owen shot up towards him. 'Penny for the guy?'

He frowned at our efforts. 'Bit early aren't you?'

'It's only two weeks away,' I said.

He shook his head and carried on. We never saw him again.

A scruffy old geezer came staggering out of the pub. Maybe it was the old lady's husband. He thought our guy was the funniest thing ever and couldn't stop laughing. He made a big fuss of rummaging through his wallet, as I nudged Andrea. Then he pulled out a coin and flipped it in the air. It landed on SpongeBob's not inconsiderable belly. It was a penny. One pence. 'Don't spend it all at once,' he snorted and weaved his way past us.

'A penny?' I frowned.

'Well, that's what we asked him for,' said Andrea.

Owen picked it up and held it between forefinger

and thumb. 'Maybe it's a magic penny that doubles every day,' he laughed.

I shook my head. 'What the heck can we buy for a penny?'

We obviously needed to up our game. When people say, 'Penny for the guy?' what they really mean is twenty pence or fifty pence or a pound.

Then weirdly, for no apparent reason, the next ten minutes were successful. One after another, people started throwing money into the cup. It was filling up nicely.

A woman pushing a fully-stacked shopping trolley halted in front of us. She frowned and tut-tutted. 'Is that you, Andrea Zabalova? Well, I must say, I'm surprised at you. Does your mother know you're out begging?'

'Begging?' said Andrea.

'That's what you're doing, isn't it?' she said, moving on.

Andrea looked a bit tearful. 'Who's the money for?' she asked me.

'What do you mean, who's it for?' I said. 'It's for us. We're the idiots standing out here in the cold. Who did you think it was for?'

We counted it. There was £5.42.

'I thought it might be for charity,' said Andrea. 'Children in Need is coming up soon. I assumed …'

'Children in Need?' I laughed. 'I'm a child in need. I was expecting a PS4 for my birthday but ended up getting Monopoly and a Roald Dahl box set instead.'

Andrea looked flustered. She apologised and said that she'd better go home.

'Wait!' I called after her. 'What about your money?'

But she'd already gone.

We stayed another half an hour. Owen tried strenuously to attract people's attention with singing, dancing and telling jokes. But we still only ended up with £7.53.

'Uh-oh,' said Owen, suddenly.

'What is it?'

'Look,' he pointed.

A gang of teenagers came clattering around the corner, making enough noise to wake the devil. They were pushing a supermarket trolley with a guy in it. It nearly toppled over as they took the corner and narrowly missed colliding with a lady pushing a pram.

Their guy was moving. I don't mean it was flopping around, I mean it was actually moving. It had a proper Guy Fawkes mask on it, but the head and body belonged to a living, breathing person, who was wearing a denim jacket and jeans.

The gang slowed down and swaggered towards us. I felt myself backing away.

'Scat!' yelled the obvious leader, kicking our pushchair over. I recognised him. It was Riley Jones's older brother, Neil. He's nowhere near as nice as Riley.

'But we were here first,' Owen protested.

'And we're here now, so get lost.'

'This is our patch,' said a stocky blond kid. 'Go and find somewhere else.' He grabbed our pushchair and scooted off with it, followed by his mates.

We chased after them into the car park behind the shops.

I couldn't believe what happened next. Riley's brother brought out a lighter and set fire to SpongeBob. Actually set fire to him.

Owen lurched forward, but I held him back.

The fire started in SpongeBob's belly and began to spread quickly. It looked like a case of spontaneous combustion. The flames spread to the mask, which gave off a foul chemical smell and melted like the witch in *The Wizard of Oz*. Where were the police when you needed them? The police station was only about thirty metres away.

Riley's brother grabbed the blazing pushchair and sprinted with it. He gave it a final big push, then released it, letting it roll right into the road. Whooping with laughter, he ran off with his gang, leaving Owen and I open-mouthed.

The blazing pushchair kept on rolling, then toppled over in the middle of Lambourne Way.

Owen stepped off the kerb towards it as a white van skidded to a halt in front of us, tyres screeching.

The driver glared at us. He virtually had steam coming out of his ears as he threw open his door.

We got the heck out of there, pronto, leaving the pushchair and SpongeBob far behind us.

As we turned a corner, I slipped and fell. The cup flew out of my hands and the coins erupted everywhere, hitting the ground with a loud chink, some spinning momentarily, two or three rolling off into the distance. I scrambled to pick them up.

'Oy, you two!' the van driver called after us, speedily approaching on foot.

Owen pulled me up and we scarpered. Taking a short cut through the park, we virtually flew up the narrow lane behind my house and then scurried along the side of my house into the back garden. We hid in my shed, trying to catch our breath.

We must have stayed there a full ten minutes while I attempted to count our remaining earnings. A grand total of forty-six pence.

The shed door suddenly opened and a shadowy figure loomed there. We both screamed like girls.

'What the heck are you up to?' said a voice. It belonged to my dad.

'Nothing,' I said, getting to my feet.

'Don't give me that. My mate Jason just rang me and said he saw you standing outside the Spar.'

'We made a guy, that's all,' I said.

Dad tried to peer past us. 'Where is it, then?'

'Some teenagers nicked it off us,' Owen explained.

We didn't mention the fire or the van.

Dad shook his head. 'I don't want you doing that, Richie.'

'All kids do it. I bet you used to do it.'

He couldn't argue with that. 'I didn't know where you were. You could get into trouble. Did you make any money?'

I held out the forty-six pence.

He quickly counted it and laughed. 'Well, I hope you and your forty-six pence will be very happy together. Next time, tell me where you're going.'

'We made the guy ourselves,' Owen boasted. 'And I sang songs and told jokes.'

Dad raised his eyebrows. 'You're on your own, Owen.'

He wandered off, leaving us to stew in our own failure.

I needed a new plan. Richard Branson, I wasn't. Yet.

£ CHAPTER FOUR £

Moneyman to the Rescue!

Later that evening, as Dad and I sat with trays on our laps watching *The X Factor*, his mobile phone went off. He frowned, then answered it. I watched as he nodded enthusiastically, his eyes growing wider by the second.

As soon as he put the phone down, he started whooping like crazy and dancing around the room.

'What is it?' I asked, bewildered.

'Your old man's gonna be on the telly,' he said, pulling me into his little dance and breaking out into the Abba song 'Money, Money, Money'.

'You're kidding?' said Mum, walking into the room, half-spilling her tea.

'I'm not. Come and give us a kiss.' She tried to run off, but he grabbed her and pulled her onto the sofa.

He explained to us that he'd have to go to a TV studio in Bristol in a few days' time.

My dad is always applying to go on quiz shows. He's been doing this for years. He has pretty impressive general knowledge. A few weeks ago, he'd made a phone call to a show called *All or Nothing*. They'd asked him five questions and he'd got them all right, so he passed the first stage. We thought nothing more of it. *All or Nothing* is a really high-profile show. I've seen people go on there and win £100,000.

'Are you definitely going on it, then?' I said. Pound signs flashed on and off like light bulbs in my head. My PS4 was suddenly looking like more than a possibility.

'Well, almost definitely. This is an audition. If they think I'm interesting enough, I can go on the actual show the following week.'

'What do you mean, interesting?'

'Well, they can't have boring people on the telly, can they?'

I prayed that he'd be interesting enough. 'If you win,' I asked him, 'can I get my PS4?'

'I haven't even got there yet.'

'But if you do?'

'I suppose so. If I win more than, say, £2,000. How about you pay £50 towards it and I'll pay the rest.'

'Fifty pounds? Of my money?'

'You've gone pale, Rich. I was only joking. Course I'll get you one. If I win, you can have three PS4s.'

*   *   *

When I woke up on Monday morning, I noticed immediately that the house was freezing cold. I could actually see my breath forming in front of me. I reached across to the radiator. It was like ice.

Throwing my dressing gown on, I headed down to the kitchen. Mum was sitting at the table, also in her dressing gown, both hands wrapped around a mug of tea.

I yawned. 'Who turned my radiator off?'

'*All* the radiators are off,' my dad called out from the utility room.

'Why?' I said to Mum. 'It's nearly winter, isn't it? Shouldn't we be having them on?'

'They're not working. The boiler's not working. That means no central heating.' She looked fed up. 'Your dad's re-setting it.'

'I've tried re-setting it five times in the last ten minutes. Nothing's happening.'

'Well try again, then,' Mum yelled.

'What do you think I'm doing?' I heard a clunk as he dropped something, then swore.

I made myself some Weetabix. Mum didn't say anything.

Ten minutes later, Dad joined us at the table.

'Well?' said Mum.

'I think it's kaput.'

She put down her mug. 'What do you mean? Please don't tell me we need a new boiler.'

'I'm not an expert but I think we might.'

'Noooo,' Mum cried. She left us and ran upstairs.

Dad put his head in his hands.

'Does a new boiler cost very much? I asked him.

He nodded. His eyes were looking watery again.

'How much?'

'About £2,000.'

I paused, my spoon halfway towards my mouth. 'What??!!'

'You heard right.'

'But that's more than you earn a month.'

'A lot more. I know.'

'How are you gonna pay it?'

Dad rested his chin on his hands. 'I guess we'll have to take out a loan.'

'But won't you have to pay interest on that?'

'Yes, we will.' He seemed impressed with my knowledge. 'So you know what interest is, then?'

'We've been finding out about it in school,' I said. 'Maybe, you'll win on the quiz. Then, we'll be rolling in it.'

He raised his eyebrows and took a sip of tea.

'You *could* win,' I said. 'You never know.'

There was no chance of that happening, apparently. Dad told me he'd rung his boss about twenty minutes ago to see if he could have a day off for the audition, but he wouldn't let him. He'd been ringing the TV studio to try and re-arrange the date, but he wasn't holding out any hope.

I told Dad that he should ring in sick and go to the audition anyway. He got really angry and said, 'Oh yeah, and what if I get through to the next stage and my boss sees me on national television? End of job.'

I couldn't see why he didn't get a different job. A better-paid job.

'You'd best get off to school, son,' he said.

He looked like all the air had been sucked out of him.

*   *   *

On the long walk to school, I gave myself a bit of a talking to. I was beginning to see how selfish I'd been. After all, my life didn't depend on me having a PS4, did it?

I backed up against a hedge to let a lady with a pram pass by. She smiled at me.

It can't be easy being a parent, I thought. I'd seen my dad close to tears twice in the last few days. My mum and dad's arguments were getting worse lately. I could see how much pressure they were under.

Mr Johnson hobbled out through his front gate and said good morning to me. One of his legs isn't real. He had to have one of his legs taken off in hospital. But he's always smiling.

Life is so unfair. Mum and Dad have to work so hard that they're exhausted and irritable and yet they still have to struggle to survive. And just when they think they're doing okay, bad things come along and happen.

A white van zoomed past me, straight over a huge puddle near the kerb, soaking my trousers. The driver beeped his horn loudly and I heard laughter.

Mr Johnson seemed to find it quite amusing.

I was determined I was going to get some money for the family fund. I would be like a superhero coming to the rescue. I would be like Robin Hood. I would be … Moneyman!

In school, I told Owen about my plans. He was keen to join in. He could be my sidekick. We'd have to think of a name for him too. We planned to use Google to find out what jobs are open to eleven-year-olds. We'd had enough of standing outside the Spar.

As luck would have it, it was pouring down with rain at lunchtime, so we were allowed on the Chromebooks.

After a bit of searching, we came up with the following options: babysitting, house cleaning, car washing, mowing lawns, raking leaves, shopping for old people, painting, selling homemade crafts, selling lemonade at drink stands, walking dogs.

Basically, it's illegal to employ a minor to do an adult's job. Kids are called minors.

By accident, we found this article about an

American kid who made himself some business cards and went around putting them through people's letterboxes offering his services for sale. Owen came back to my house with me. We got straight onto Publisher and started designing some of our *own* business cards. We printed them off and cut them out.

That Saturday afternoon, the pair of us went around knocking on doors on our estate. As each door opened, I gave the person who opened the door one of our cards and Owen did the talking, which he is good at. He made an elaborate bow each time and announced grandly, 'How do you do, Sir/Madam. Good afternoon to you. We live in the neighbourhood and have just set up in business. Can we help you with any of the following jobs?'

I then read out the list and gave them one of our cards.

It didn't go according to plan.

Kind-faced Mrs Drew at Number 47 said, 'Well, you could mow my lawn … if it wasn't soaking wet from the frost.'

Miss Pike at Number 33 said, 'Sorry, sweetheart, I

have a lovely neighbour and he does all my odd jobs for me, you see.'

Grumpy old Mr Watkins from the flats across the road told us, 'The cub scouts and brownies do jobs for free.'

One bloke got really uppity. 'I used to be a policeman,' he said. 'Isn't it illegal for kids of your age to be doing this? You're only minors.'

Owen's response to this was, 'I've never been down a mine in my life. We're not living in Victorian times, y'know.'

The bloke didn't appreciate the humour, so we quickly retreated.

When we asked one old biddy who'd forgotten to put her teeth in if she wanted us to go to the Spar for her and get some bread or milk, she eyed us suspiciously and said, 'How do I know you won't run off with my money?'

What a nerve! Did we look like criminals?

One old man thought I was his grandson and invited us in. We didn't go.

In the last house that we called at, as I reached for the gate, a giant Alsatian appeared over the top of it and tried to bite our heads off. We nearly fell into the road. It put me right off any thoughts of being a postman.

Our business lasted one afternoon. People are just weird, especially old people.

I was so desperate to make some money, I seriously contemplated pretending I had a seriously ill relative and that we were collecting money so that they could go on holiday to Florida and swim with the dolphins.

I wondered how much money Raj had managed to make with his lemonade.

*   *   *

My superhero idea hadn't got off to a good start. I was really trying hard to be good and helpful. If God knows that your intentions are good, why can't he help out? It's really frustrating.

I switched plans. I decided that borrowing was the answer. If I borrowed enough money from enough people, then I could buy loads of cheap stuff in Poundland and sell it in school at a profit.

Don't get me wrong, I'm not thick. I do understand that if you borrow something, you have to pay it back.

But I was completely confident I could make loads of money.

I started with my family. Not Mum and Dad, of course. I nabbed hold of Granddad when he was up at his allotment, which is not far from our house. He goes there once a week to chill and chat with his friends.

'Alright, Sunny Jim?' he said, spotting me. 'Come to give us a hand, have you?' He was sitting on a little bench, smoking his pipe, like Gandalf. He's not allowed to smoke it in the house.

'Uh, sorry, I'm kind of busy, Granddad.'

'Oh, right. Expect you've got homework. We didn't used to have homework when I was in school.'

They didn't have computers either. I'm not even sure they had pens.

'Granddad?' I said. 'I was wondering if you could, sort of, lend me some money?'

He looked puzzled. 'What for?'

I hadn't been expecting questions. 'It's sort of a secret.'

He laughed. 'Got a girlfriend, have you? Women can be expensive. Is it that Slovakian girl, Andrea? She's a pretty girl. It's not Valentine's Day until

February, y'know, although Christmas is not too far away.'

Boy, he didn't half ramble on. I pulled a face. 'Granddad! She's not my girlfriend. She's just my friend.'

His head went back. 'Not your girlfriend? Well you need to get one, then. You're not getting any younger. I've got one, y'know.'

He did, too. Mrs Cledge, from up the road. She wasn't exactly a looker.

'Do I have to tell you what the money's for?' I said.

He frowned. 'If you want *my* money, you do. I'm not made of money y'know.'

I knew he was retired but he had something called a pension, which meant that he got money every week.

'How much do you need?' he asked.

'How much have you got to spare?'

He pulled a ten pound note from his pocket and dangled it there. It wasn't exactly the kind of money I was thinking of.

'Okay,' I said, grabbing it off him. 'Thanks, Granddad.'

'Oy,' he called after me. 'Don't forget to give it back. It's a loan, not a gift.'

Within a few hours, the tenner was gone. There's a McDonald's on the main road not far from my house. That evening, while I was out playing with Owen, I had the sudden urge to buy us some Big Macs and Smarties McFlurries. I felt sick afterwards, in more ways than one.

That same evening, I knocked on Danielle's bedroom door.

'WHATTT!!' This is her usual window-shaking response.

I sidled a few centimetres into her room.

A very short conversation ensued:

'Sis, can I borrow some money?'

'What for?'

'I wanna buy Mum a present.'

'Nah. Don't be weird.'

Conversation over.

*　*　*

The next day, I told Owen about my failed attempts at borrowing.

He laughed. 'I can lend you money, if you like.'

My eyes lit up. 'How much?'

'Everything.'

'Everything?'

'You can have all the money I own. Hold out your hand.'

I held out my hand and he placed twenty-three pence into it.

'Gee, thanks.'

'You're welcome.'

'Is that seriously all the money you have?'

'Yup.'

'Don't you get pocket money?'

'Nope.'

I couldn't understand why he was still smiling.

'Haven't you got any birthday money or Christmas money saved up?'

'We're Jehovah's Witnesses,' he said. 'We don't celebrate Christmas.'

How come I didn't know this? 'You mean you don't get Christmas presents?'

'Not from my mum and dad.'

I couldn't understand how he managed to stay so chirpy. He had to be one of the happiest people alive.

'I know someone who lends money,' he said, 'but it's probably not a good idea. He's not a very nice person.'

'Who?' I said.

'Riley's brother, Neil.'

'The one who set fire to SpongeBob?'

This idea had alarm bells all over it, but my superhero radar couldn't have been working properly because I went ahead with it anyway.

CHAPTER FIVE

The Borrowers

Neil Jones is probably the scariest kid on the estate. He's only sixteen but even the police seem scared of him. His dad is pretty scary too. He's been in prison for assault.

Despite knowing all this, I was determined to raise some funds so I could start making some money.

The following evening, not long after I'd got in from school, Owen texted saying that he'd seen Neil and his gang in the park. I sprang into action. I texted Owen back, telling him my plan, and he agreed to come with me.

When we got there, a mother and toddler were leaving in disgust as one of Neil's gang was in the process of wrecking the swings. There was nobody on them thankfully. This nutter was pushing one of the swings higher and higher, higher than it was supposed to go. He leapt into the air for his final, mighty push. The seat flew right over the top of the frame and kept looping around and around the bar, the chains getting shorter and shorter until there was no more left.

To the right of the swings, I noticed a *No Litter* signpost that somebody – guess who – had wrapped a supermarket trolley around.

Neil's short, stocky blond friend spotted us straight away … 'Hey look, it's SpongeBob's two little friends. How's SpongeBob doing? Did he need plastic surgery?'

A little voice in my head asked me if I was sure I wanted to do this.

However, I needed some money so I could make more money and carry out my superhero mission of saving my family. I had £50 birthday money, but that was already in my savings account, where Dad was keeping a close eye on it. Other than that, I had £15 to my name – hardly enough to build a fortune.

Taking a deep breath, I moved forward.

Neil frowned. 'What do you want?'

'He wants to lose weight,' said Blondie. 'That's what he wants. You ought to cut down on the McDonald's, mate.'

I hesitated, then said, 'I need to borrow some money.'

Neil smirked. 'And?'

'Somebody told me you lend money,' I said.

He stood up, eyes narrowed. 'Who told you that? I bet it was my moron of a brother. I'll kill 'im.'

I backed into Owen, standing on his toes.

Neil glanced around, furtively. 'How much do you want?' he said, pulling a wad of twenties from his pocket. There had to be a few hundred pounds there. Did he and his gang rob banks for a living?

'What's the maximum?' I said, keeping my nerve.

'What are you planning to buy, a Ferrari?' Blondie laughed.

'How much do you want?' Neil repeated. He looked irritated.

'Pig alert,' one of his mates said.

I thought they were talking about my weight.

Owen nudged me. Two community police officers were heading towards us from the direction of the canal.

Riley's brother quickly stashed the roll of money away.

The CPOs didn't look very scary. One was about

three feet tall and the other looked about twelve years old and had spots.

They had a good look around, taking in the swing and supermarket trolley. 'Alright lads? What are you up to, then?'

Nobody said anything.

'Why do you always think we're up to something?' said Blondie.

The short policeman laughed. 'Let's be honest, you normally are.'

Neil looked mortally offended. 'That's slander,' he said.

The spotty policeman pointed at the trolley. 'Your handiwork?'

'Huh?' said Blondie.

'Been busy, have we?'

'Dunno, have we?'

The CPOs became serious. 'You do realise that this park is for children aged under twelve. Look at the sign over there.' This one didn't have a trolley attached to it.

'Hey,' said Neil. 'We were going for a walk, that's all. Walking's not against the law, is it? We stopped when we saw you.'

'Feeling guilty, were you?'

Neil shook his head. 'C'mon lads, let's go somewhere where we won't be harassed.'

The short CPO reddened. 'We weren't harassing you.'

'Nah, of course you weren't. We're all just having a nice little friendly chat, aren't we?'

Neil and his mates headed for the canal.

I didn't have my money yet, so I scurried after them, Owen following.

The short CPO grabbed my elbow. 'Are you sure you want to go with them?'

I shook him off.

'That's assault, that is,' Neil called back.

As we left the park, I turned back to see the policemen attempting to lift the trolley over the signpost. Mission impossible.

We headed for the canal. Another trolley sat, half-submerged, in it. There was also a generous sprinkling of cans and bottles.

We slowed down at an old bridge and followed the towpath underneath.

It was dark and there was a very unpleasant smell. Two of Neil's gang took a pee in the canal, competing to see who could reach the furthest. Meanwhile, Blondie graffitied some really rude words on the underside of the bridge.

Neil took out the wad of money again. 'So how much do you want?'

'Fifty?' I ventured.

'Is that all? Why not make it a hundred?'

'Really?'

'Really.'

'Sign this.' He gave me a card. It had lots of tiny writing on it, which I couldn't read properly in the dark.

'What is it?' I said.

'It's a contract.'

'Don't,' said Owen.

I signed it and another one too. Neil kept one of them and gave one back to me. Then he handed some notes over.

'Better count them,' he laughed.

I counted five twenties.

'Happy?' he smirked.

I nodded.

He made me shake hands with him.

Owen and I started to head off when two of them

suddenly grabbed Owen, dragged him up to the top of the bridge and dangled him over the edge. I've never heard anyone yell so loud. There was genuine panic in his voice.

'What are you doing?' I gasped.

'What does it look like?' Neil smirked. 'We're dangling your mate off the bridge. Give us £100 and we'll let him go.'

I felt myself turn white. 'You're joking.'

He put his face right up to mine, nose to nose. His breath reeked of fags. 'Yeah, we are.'

They all broke into laughter as his mates pulled Owen back up.

'No holding hands, now,' one of them called out as we ran off.

'Are you okay?' I asked Owen, who was wiping his nose in his jacket sleeve.

'This is not good,' he said. 'Let me look at that card.'

I took it out of my pocket. On one side it said, *I agree to pay back the amount of £100 at a rate of 10% interest every day.*

'Now you've gone and done it,' Owen said.

* * *

The week passed quite quickly. I hadn't really thought through my idea of buying things from Poundland and then selling them. Poundland was in the town centre. How was I going to get there on a weekday?

And so the £100 I'd borrowed lay hidden inside one of my socks for five days, busily doing nothing.

Friday was Raj's birthday party. I'd been invited, but I didn't really want to go. He'd invited everybody else in the class. All twenty-five of us.

In school, he'd brought in chocolate éclairs for everyone.

'What have you bought Raj for his birthday?' Andrea asked me on the way home.

'What do you mean?' I said. 'I haven't bought him anything. He's not my mate, is he?'

Andrea shrugged. 'He's not really my friend either but I am going to his party, and so are you.'

'What have *you* bought him, then?'

'A book of sudoku puzzles. He likes those.'

It really bugged me that I was expected to buy him a present. He's as rich as a prince. He doesn't need stuff.

'I'm not buying him anything,' I repeated.

Owen told me over the phone that he'd bought

Raj a massive bar of Galaxy chocolate, 'because Raj is interested in outer space'. Random.

It looked like I'd be the only one not buying him a present. I didn't want people talking about me. I had to get something.

It was then that I did something really stupid. I decided that, rather than get nothing, I would outdo everyone else in the present stakes. I bought a pop-up birthday card and put twenty pounds inside it. Yes, you heard right, *twenty* pounds.

* * *

Raj's party was at a local golf club. My mum dropped me off.

'Ooh, this is posh!' she exclaimed, admiring all the decorations. Raj's parents had gone completely overboard.

'Isn't that a TV camera?' Mum pointed.

It was. And there was more than one. At first, I thought they might be there for a golf tournament but, as it turned out, they were there for Raj. He was taking part in a programme called *Rich Kids' Parties*. We were *all* taking part in it.

Inside, most of the boys had ties and waistcoats on. They looked like snooker players. Owen and I were the only boys without ties. The girls all had their best party frocks on. Andrea looked really nice.

The hall looked spectacular. The theme was Outer Space and there were stars and planets everywhere. Even I had to admit, it was pretty dazzling.

Off to one side was a huge display of food from all around the world.

In front of the stage was a mountain of birthday presents.

Suddenly, a whoop of excitement broke out and everybody rushed outside. I thought maybe a celebrity had arrived.

A white stretch limo pulled up. Out popped Raj's mum and dad, dressed and acting like celebrities, followed by Raj, who was wearing a white suit. To be fair to him, he looked a little bit embarrassed. The TV people insisted on filming him getting out of the car twice. Then they made us all sing 'Happy Birthday' three times.

When we got back inside, there was a band on stage called Big Mac's Wholly Soul Band. There were about ten of them. They had guitars, drums, keyboards, trumpets and trombones and they made a lot of noise.

The girls started dancing straight away while most of the boys stood in clusters looking slightly embarrassed. There was no way I was going to dance.

There was a ton of food. I ate so much I felt sick. Owen actually *was* sick, after eating too many pink wafery biscuits.

The music stopped briefly while Raj's dad made a little speech. He thanked everyone for coming, then told them how special his son was and about how, one day, Raj would take over the family business. Then he and his wife presented Raj with a brand new Apple computer. I know for a fact it cost over a thousand pounds.

When the fuss had died down a bit, I sidled over to Raj and gave him his card.

'Thanks,' he said. 'Shall I open it now?'

I nodded.

It was quite a funny card. Rodney and Del Boy from *Only Fools and Horses* were on the front of it. As Raj opened it, two ten pound notes floated to the floor.

He picked them up, looking confused.

His mum was standing nearby. She looked equally baffled. 'That's very generous of your parents,' she said.

'It's not from them,' I insisted. 'It's from me.'

She frowned. 'Are you sure they know about this?'

It was almost as if she thought I didn't have the right to give someone twenty pounds. Only *her* family could splash their money around.

I shrugged. 'It's only money.'

'Well, thank you very much,' she said, starting to walk away. 'I hope you're enjoying the party.'

'Thanks, mate,' Raj said, shaking my hand enthusiastically.

Owen emerged from the toilets, looking confused. 'What was all that about?' he said.

I chose not to tell him.

The party ended with a spectacular fireworks display outside and then, on the way out, in a weird sort of reversal, *we* were all given presents. Not cheap presents, either. The girls were given bracelets and the boys watches. I have no idea how much they cost, but they weren't plastic ones.

*   *   *

When we got home, as I climbed out of the car, I spotted something on the ground next to one of the front wheels.

'What is it?' asked Mum, as I knelt down to retrieve it.

'Looks like a wallet.' It was a nice one too, real leather.

We took it inside to the kitchen. There was mess everywhere. My dad was trying to fix the washing machine.

'Any luck?' Mum asked him.

Sweat beaded his brow. 'I hate to say this, but I think we might need a new one.'

'Please don't say that,' she said.

'Well, what can I say? We *have* had it over ten years. It's old and clapped out. A bit like me.'

Mum held up the wallet. 'Look what Rich just found.'

He didn't notice it at first. When he saw what it was, he joined us at the table. 'Is there any money in it?'

There was quite a lot of money in it as it turned out, all new and crisp notes, as if someone had just come from the cashpoint machine. Mum counted it. There was £163.50 in there.

My eyes lit up.

My dad must have spotted the greedy look. 'Don't even think about it,' he said. 'We can't keep it.'

I pulled a face. 'Why not? It's not as if we stole it. I found it.'

'It belongs to someone else,' he said, firmly. There were about five plastic cards in there, which Dad flicked through. 'It belongs to an E Millinship.'

'Do you know him?' Mum asked.

'Nope. I guess we'd better hand it in to the police.'

'Don't be daft,' I said. 'They'll just keep it.'

'Richie!' Mum gasped.

I glanced over at the mess on the floor. 'Look, Dad, you said yourself that we might need a new washing machine. And a new boiler. Don't you think Lady Luck left the wallet there for us because she knows we need the money?'

Dad gave me a look. 'No, I don't. This poor man or woman is probably going frantic at the moment. They might need this money to pay their bills. What if I lost *my* wallet? I would hope someone would have the decency to hand it in.'

'You're too nice,' I said in frustration. 'No wonder we haven't got any money.'

Mum laughed. 'Didn't know it was possible to be *too* nice.' She glanced through the cards. 'Look, it's got the address on here.' It was a library card. 'Whoever it is lives on Monnow Way.'

'But doesn't part of you want to keep it?' I said, unable to hide my frustration.

'Of course, but we're not going to, because we're decent people.'

'Yeah, decent, poor people.'

'We're not poor,' Mum frowned. 'There are loads of people worse off than us. Some people haven't even got a roof over their heads.'

'I think I'll take it back right now,' said Dad. He placed the cards and money back in the wallet and headed out to the car.

Mum made me help her with the washing up. She shook her head.

'What?' I said.

'I think you upset your dad, just then.'

'Why?'

'Well, we brought you up to be honest.'

'But we need the money.'

'But it wasn't our money.'

A few minutes later, Dad's car pulled up outside.

'Did you know him?' Mum asked.

'No, not really, I've seen him on the estate, walking his dog. It was an old chap, called Eddie. He was very grateful. He offered me a cup of tea.'

'Cup of tea!' I spluttered. 'You just gave him £163.50.'

'It was *his* money.'

'Didn't he give you a reward?' I said.

'He tried to give me a tenner, but I wouldn't take it. He and his wife were very sweet. I'm glad I gave it to them.'

I shook my head, threw my empty mug into the washing-up bowl and headed upstairs. I don't normally pray but I lay in bed, staring up at the ceiling, thinking that now might be a good time to start.

£ CHAPTER SIX £

Desperate Measures

It turned out that the washing machine was fixable, but we would definitely need a new boiler. After a week or so, we still hadn't had it replaced. Dad was ringing around, trying to find a good estimate.

Meanwhile, our house was like an igloo. It felt warmer outside than in. I had to wear thermal underwear, two pairs of socks and two jumpers. The weather wasn't getting any warmer either.

I was beginning to understand what my dad had said about what you *need* being more important than what you *want*. Right then, a new boiler seemed far more important to me than any PS4. I needed to be warm.

*   *   *

The following Tuesday, Owen and I were on our way home from school, taking our usual shortcut up the narrow alleyway behind my house.

Halfway up it, he gave me a nudge. 'Hey, get a move on, I think we're being followed.'

'Don't be daft,' I said, glancing over my shoulder. 'We're not in a film, y'know.'

'Don't you recognise them?' he said. 'That's two of Thingy's gang.'

'What do they want?'

'Dunno, keep moving.'

We broke into a run, which wasn't easy as the lane was so steep. Just as we reached the top, our exit was blocked by none other than Neil Jones himself, accompanied by one of his drongo mates.

We spun around. Our pursuers were closing in on us. They had us hemmed in.

'What's up?' I said, nervously.

Neil perched himself on a garden wall. 'Nothing. Just come for a friendly chat, that's all, in case you need reminding how much you borrowed from me seven days ago.'

'I know. I'm gonna pay you back next week.'

'Really? You must be made of money.'

'If he was made of money,' said Owen, 'he wouldn't be borrowing.'

One of the gang promptly grabbed him and bounced him off a fence.

Neil took out one of his cards and pointed at it. 'I take it you've read the small print.'

'To be honest,' I lied, 'I threw the card in the bin. I didn't want my dad to know I'd been borrowing money.'

He pretended to look offended. 'Chucked it in the bin?' He handed me another one. 'Read it this time, especially the bit about 10% interest.'

'What does it mean?' I said, pretending not to know.

He gave a little snort. 'It means this. You borrowed the £100 last Tuesday. So, on the Wednesday, you owed me £110.' He was using the calculator on his phone. 'Thursday, you owed me £121. Friday, you owed me £133.10. Saturday, you owed me £146.41. Sunday, you owed me £161.05. Monday £177.15 . Tuesday £196.48 and, as of today, a grand total of £194.86.'

Owen gasped. 'But that's nearly £200. He only borrowed a hundred.'

'Clever boy,' Neil said, patting him on the shoulder.

'That's how interest works. By next week, it'll be more like £400.'

'I'll pay you tomorrow,' I said, not really knowing how I was going to do it. After splashing out on Raj's present, I had nothing – apart from my birthday savings.

Neil did some more calculations. 'If you pay me tomorrow, it'll be £214.34. But, as I like you so much, we'll call it £214.'

I felt sick to the stomach.

He stood up and flicked my right cheek. 'See you by the canal bridge at six. Be there.'

Blondie bounced Owen off the fence again just for the fun of it.

We watched them head off down the lane. One of them launched an empty beer can over the fence into someone's garden.

'Holy mackerel!' Owen gasped. 'I told you not to borrow from him.'

'What do you mean?' I said. 'It was *you* who told me all about him.'

'Did I?'

'Yes, you did.' I glanced around nervously. 'What do you think will happen if I don't pay him?'

Owen's face turned a deathly white. 'Don't even think like that. I know someone who tried that once.'

'What happened?'

'Something very bad.'

'Like what?'

'Do you remember Joel Yalland?'

'Yeah, he got hit by a bus.'

'Well, it wasn't an accident. I heard he was standing at a bus stop and somebody pushed him out into the road.'

'But that's attempted murder.'

'I know. Luckily, he only had a broken leg.'

'Only?'

I broke out in a cold sweat.

Sleep didn't come easy that night. I kept dreaming about buses.

*　　*　　*

I can't pretend I'm not ashamed of what I did next. Basically, I took something that didn't belong to me. I'm nearly eleven years old. I know stealing is wrong, believe me, but my family needed money. I was desperate.

The whole PS4 dream had pretty much gone out of the window. Now, I was trying to save my mum and dad's marriage. They hadn't stopped arguing since the combined problems with the washing machine and the boiler. I spent most of my time creeping around the house, trying to stay out of their way. My dad looked as though someone had given him a beating. Mum had forgotten how to smile. Danielle kept out of the way too and Granddad stayed in his room, wrapped up. The cold air wasn't doing his chest any good.

That afternoon, it was almost as if God set me up to steal. He planted the money right there in front of me.

It happened just after lunch. Normally, Riley takes the register to the office when Miss has finished with it, but Riley wasn't in. Miss was looking for someone else to take it and I caught her eye. I asked if Owen could come with me, but she said, 'Don't be daft, you're old enough to go on your own.'

I strolled through the hall where the Reception kids were doing PE. At least half of them were in their underpants and vests. They were very quiet and well-behaved, much quieter than Year Six.

As I turned into the office, Leah from Year Five came rushing out, knocking the register out of my hand. She ran off, without saying sorry.

The office was empty and dead quiet.

We have two school secretaries – Mrs Scott and Mrs Archer. Neither of them was in there.

And then I spotted it.

The money.

A black, metal box with its lid open, sat on one of the desks. Inside were lots of coins and a roll of notes wrapped in an elastic band.

Today had been non-uniform day. When it's non-uniform day, we all have to bring in a pound each. That was obviously the money in the black box, which was staring up at me, calling out to me almost.

My heart drummed against my ribcage.

Nobody would know it was me. There were no CCTV cameras. People are constantly coming and going in the office. It could be anybody.

If I wanted to avoid ending up under a bus, I'd have to pay Neil Jones his money, one way or another.

I can't believe that I'm confessing to this. I promise I'm not proud of it.

I stuck my head out into the corridor, to see if

anyone was coming. It was all clear. My hand shot out as fast as a cobra and stashed the roll of notes in my pocket. Then I marched briskly out of the office.

I noticed the register was still on the floor and bent down to pick it up.

As I straightened up, Miss Satchell, our teaching assistant, was right there in front of me. She laughed and pointed. 'Where are you going with that?'

I nearly had a heart attack. 'With what?' I gulped.

'With that,' she pointed. 'Aren't you supposed to be taking it back?'

I looked down.

'Daydreamer,' she said, taking it off me. 'I'll take it. Are you okay, Richie? You look a bit pale.'

I headed straight to the toilets. I shot into a cubicle and pulled the latch across. I thought I might vomit.

I couldn't leave the roll in my pocket. Someone might spot it. I took the elastic band off it and flattened the money out against the wall. I counted it. There was £120. It still wasn't enough to pay off my debt, but it would make a dent in it.

Slipping my right shoe off, I laid the notes flat out inside it, then inserted my foot on top of it. I made my way back into the classroom with a lopsided limp.

Mrs Lloyd spotted me straight away. 'Where've you been, Richie, Timbuktu?'

'I needed the toilet.'

Now I felt like I actually *did* need the toilet. Number one *and* number two at the same time.

About half an hour later the class phone went off, causing my heart to nearly leap from my ribcage. All the classrooms in our school have wall-mounted phones near the doors. I sit right next to the door.

Mrs Lloyd trotted over and picked it up. She pulled a few faces and said, 'Oh,' and 'Oh dear,' a lot, followed by 'Really?' and then, 'Rightio'. She placed the phone back in its cradle and announced that there was to be a class assembly straight away. Everyone began muttering. We'd already had one assembly today.

My right foot felt pretty uncomfortable as we filed into the hall.

We sang a song about being kind, which we sing quite regularly, called 'Pass it On'. Then our headteacher, Mrs Davies, spoke.

'I'm afraid I have some very sad news, children,' she said.

'Did someone die?' Owen whispered to me.

I wanted to dig a big hole and jump into it.

'As you know,' said Mrs Davies, 'it's non-uniform day today and you've all very kindly brought in your money …'

My dinner was trying to come back up through my throat.

'… which we're going to donate to Children in Need in a few weeks' time.'

A groan escaped from my lips, thankfully not too loud. Owen laughed at me and shook his head.

My heart sank. I had no idea the money was for charity. Nobody had mentioned that or, if they had, I hadn't been listening.

Mrs Davies paused for dramatic effect. 'Well, we *were* going to give it to charity. Only, unfortunately, this afternoon, the money was left briefly unattended in the office …' She glanced across at Mrs Scott who was very red-faced and looked as if she also wanted to dig a hole and jump right into it. '… And, I'm afraid, it's gone.'

Gasps reverberated around the hall.

'Of course, we are hoping that somebody accidentally picked it up and that they will return it.'

'Accidentally?' hissed Owen. 'Oh yeah.'

'Do you have something to say, boys?' Mrs Davies called across in our direction.

All eyes shot towards us. I wanted to kill Owen. We both shook our heads.

'We are certainly hoping that nobody has taken it deliberately, because that would be stealing.'

No kidding.

She was speaking posher than she normally does and sounded a bit like the Queen. She was certainly not amused. 'And we don't steal in Nant-y-felin, do we, children?' 'No, Mrs Davies,' we all chanted. At least one of us was lying.

She started consulting with her deputy, Miss George. Everybody saw this as a cue to start talking. There was an excited buzz in the hall.

Owen nudged me hard. 'You don't think it was one of the teachers, do you?' he said. 'They don't earn a lot of money, y'know.'

Mrs Davies raised her arm for everyone to stop talking. 'As it's such a lot of money,' she said, 'we may have to take the unusual step of asking everyone to bring their coats and bags into the classrooms and empty them.'

Thank God I'd put it in my shoe. Nobody was going to search shoes. This was a school after all, not an airport.

'I'm hoping,' she said, 'that whoever took it will realise that they've done a very bad thing and that they will have the good conscience to return it.'

I had an image of a little angel with a halo perched on one of my shoulders, wagging a finger at me, telling me that I was evil and that I would go to hell. The little devil with the pitchfork on the other shoulder was telling me that if I didn't keep the money and pay off my debt, I would end up under a double-decker bus.

Back in class, people couldn't stop talking about the theft. I heard lots of people say how disgusting it was, the worst thing ever, lower than low.

Miss brought up a video on YouTube, just to remind us all what Children in Need was all about. Some of the girls cried. I nearly cried, too, but for a different reason.

'Listen,' said Mrs Lloyd after it had finished, 'I know it couldn't possibly have been anybody in here who took the money because you're all old enough to know right from wrong.'

Owen snorted. 'Does she think one of the infants nicked it, then?'

It was no fun during afternoon break, limping around with the money in my shoe. I felt weighed down with guilt. I imagined a sign on my back saying *Thief and Low-Life*.

A few of the boys thought it was pretty cool that someone had had the guts to walk into the office and take the money. It was almost like robbing a bank, they said.

Owen started singing the theme tune to *Mission Impossible*. He was still half-convinced a teacher had taken it. 'Just look at their cars,' he pointed. 'Teachers are on rubbish money, teaching assistants even less. I bet one of them took it. Or maybe even Mrs Scott or Mrs Archer. Or maybe even Mrs Davies? What do you think, Rich?'

I was in such a panic that I'd lost the ability to talk.

'Are you okay?' he said. 'You've gone pale. Hey, it wasn't you, was it?' He punched me in the arm.

I tried to laugh. 'Don't be daft.'

He grabbed me around the neck and we started rolling around on the ground in a play-fight which was seconds away from turning into a real one.

Then my shoe came off.

I quickly grabbed hold of it and pulled it towards my chest. I must have looked a right idiot. Owen looked bemused.

Then I realised that the shoe with the money in was still on my foot.

Back in class, my heart was racing at a million miles per hour.

For some reason, Mrs Davies never carried out her search threat.

Just before home-time, I asked Miss if I could go to the toilet. For one second, I thought she wasn't going to let me.

I took the money out of my shoe. It was damp with sweat. I rolled it back up in the elastic band, then carefully placed it on the floor behind the toilet, hoping that one of the cleaners or the caretaker would find it and hand it in.

I felt lower than low. Despicable me.

I still owed £214. Tomorrow it would be even more.

I chose to avoid my appointment at the canal bridge.

At about 6.30, my mum asked me to close the

living room curtains. I walked over to them, reached across and then backed away.

'Are you okay?' she said.

Three teenagers were sitting on our front garden wall. Two of them were smoking.

Dad joined me at the curtains. 'Cheeky blighters,' he said, heading for the front door. I hovered in the hallway.

'Oy!' my dad called out. 'Do you mind!?'

'Mind what, mate?' said Neil Jones.

'I'm not your mate. Clear off.'

Blondie spoke. 'We're not doing any harm. It's a free country.'

'Maybe it is, but that's my wall you're sitting on. It's called private property. Move on or I'll call the police.'

Neil stood up. 'We've come to call for Richie.'

I could sense the confusion in Dad's pause. 'Really? I doubt it. You're Neil Jones, aren't you?'

'So?'

'I've heard all about you.'

'Hey,' laughed Blondie. 'You're famous, Jonesy.'

Neil pointed at the house. 'Your son has got something of ours.'

My dad paused. 'I don't think so.'

'Go ask him yourself.'

'I will, after you're gone. Listen, I'll be back out in five minutes. If you're not gone, I'm calling the police.'

They made rude signs behind his back.

Dad came back in and shut the door. 'Tell me you don't hang about with them.'

'No, Dad.'

'They said you've got something of theirs.'

'I haven't, honest.'

He gave me a look. 'I hope that's true.'

'Of course.'

So now I was a thief *and* a liar. I was slowly working my way through the ten commandments.

£ CHAPTER SEVEN £

All or Nothing

"Well, we're almost coming to the end of our little mini-topic about money,' announced Mrs Lloyd.

Thank God for that, I thought. I'd learned quite enough about money. And my money problems still weren't over yet.

'Today's lesson is all about choices,' she said.

'I choose to do PE,' Owen announced.

'I'm afraid not, Owen. Nice try. That's tomorrow. Anyway, have a think about choices. All of us have to make choices every day: what to wear, how to spend our free time, which book to read. Each day is filled with options. We have to make decisions. The more decisions we make, the more experienced and confident we get at making decisions.'

I'd certainly made some really stupid choices and decisions lately.

'Some of the choices we make involve money. For example, imagine you've got three pounds and you're standing in the queue at the chip shop. What do you do with your money?'

'That's easy,' said Owen. 'Mars Bar in batter.'

Miss pulled a face. 'Really? Do they actually serve that?

'Oh yeah,' said most of the class.

'Anyway, money is limited. People have to make spending choices. What I'd like you to do is to take two minutes and make a list of some things that you would really like to have.'

My classmates took it in turns to read out their lists which, predictably, included things like PS4s, bikes, DVDs, iPods, iPads, clothes, musical instruments and games.

I hid mine in my desk. It said: *Boiler, washing machine, time machine.*

I needed to go back in time at least two weeks.

'Sometimes,' said Mrs Lloyd, 'people have to choose between buying a few inexpensive items or one expensive item. The chances are this will be very difficult because you may really want to have all of them.

'Now, look at your list. Think about each item on it, coming up with reasons to buy it and reasons not to buy it.'

I didn't get it. If it was on your list, why would you *not* want to buy it? I said as much.

'Ooh, I don't know. Maybe it costs too much money. Maybe your friend has got one and you could borrow it from him or her. Maybe you have something like it already. Ask yourself some questions. Do I need to buy this right now? Would it cost less somewhere else? Will it cost less in a few months?'

Unbelievably, she used a PS4 as an example: 'A PS4 costs a lot of money, about £434.99 I believe, but, on Amazon, you can get one for £347. Will it cost less in a few months time? Could you share somebody else's?'

I couldn't be bothered thinking about PS4s.

All I could think about was that I now owed Neil Jones £235.77. I felt like a huge triple-decker bus was coming towards me. My legs began to tingle.

*   *   *

A massive shock awaited me when I got home. A would-be contestant on *All or Nothing* had had a serious accident and they wanted to know if my dad would take his place the following evening in their Bristol studio.

No audition was necessary.

It was a no-brainer. Dad jumped at the chance. He no longer seemed concerned about his boss. He said he'd work two extra shifts to make up for it.

It turned out that family members were invited to the show too. We could sit in the audience if we wanted to.

So, Friday evening, we found ourselves in a warm TV studio.

I now owed Riley's brother £259.34, but he was thirty miles away.

The studio looked a lot smaller than it did on the telly. There were only about fifty people in the audience, most of them family members of the participants.

There were five contestants in all, one of them being my dad. Every time one of them got a question right, money accumulated in their collective pot. At the end of each round, the person with the lowest individual score was knocked out.

The first to get eliminated was this seriously

overweight guy, who was obviously nervous and sweating like a pig. He couldn't seem to get anything right.

A middle-aged lady with a posh accent was next to go. I heard her complaining on the way out that too many of the questions were about TV programmes. She claimed not to have a telly. She said she didn't believe in them.

I thought that was stupid. You don't have to *believe* in them, do you, you just watch them! She hadn't even heard of *The Simpsons*. I couldn't work out how she'd heard of *All or Nothing* if she didn't have a telly.

There were three contestants left. Dad was doing well. He knows lots of weird, random stuff, like the capital of Luxembourg and how many there are in a baker's dozen.

There was an old lady called Madge standing to his right, who hadn't got a question wrong yet. She seemed to know everything about everything. She was bound to get into the final.

Who would be joining her though – my dad or this nineteen-year-old girl called Karen, who kept giggling all the time? Finally, she stopped giggling and turned bright red when an answer she was obviously 100% sure was right turned out to be wrong. 'That's what I meant,' she said, highly flustered. 'I didn't mean to say Iceland, I meant Greenland.'

The presenter, John Craven, shook his head. 'I'm sorry Karen, we have to take your first answer.'

They played some loud music while they virtually dragged her off the set.

There was £30,000 in the pot.

My dad and Madge smiled at each other and shook hands. I heard my dad say, 'Good luck, luv.'

I shook my head. Why did he go and say that? It was *our* family who needed the luck.

The final wasn't about general knowledge. In fact, there were no more questions. The final was all about nerve. Who could hold their nerve?

Dad and Madge had to face one another, about five metres apart, each standing behind a podium. On each podium were two large buzzers, a silver one labelled SHARE and a gold one labelled KEEP.

There would be a countdown from ten to zero. On zero, they each had to hit one of their two buzzers.

If they both hit SHARE, then they would each get half of the prize money.

If one of them hit KEEP and the other hit SHARE, the person who hit KEEP would have *all* the money and the other would have nothing.

If they both hit KEEP, nobody would get anything.

The presenter had a chat with each of them, asking them what they would do with the money if they won. Dad said he'd use it to get a new car and pay for a nice holiday to Spain. He didn't mention the boiler or the washing machine.

John Craven opened a sparkly suitcase, displaying rows and rows of notes.

Thirty thousand pounds.

More than enough to pay off my debt.

My family's life was about to change.

Dad and Madge were allowed one minute to talk to each other in front of the audience. They had to state what their intentions were.

'Press KEEP, press KEEP,' I muttered, under my breath. 'She's bound to hit SHARE.'

'What do you think, luv?' said Madge, who looked like everyone's idea of a kindly old granny.

My dad smiled. 'I don't know about you, my dear, but I'd be more than happy with £15,000. That's a lot of money for my family. We could do a lot with it.'

Nice bluffing, Dad, I thought. Keep her stringing along.

'I agree, luv,' said Madge. 'I haven't got much money since my husband died. My pension doesn't go very far. If we both hit SHARE, then at least we both come away with something and we haven't had a wasted journey.'

Dad nodded. 'Are you sure, now?'

'Definitely.'

'Shall we shake hands on it?'

Nice touch, Dad. Now she's bound to believe you.

They left their podiums briefly and met in the middle.

'Well,' said the presenter, sending them back again, 'I hope you've made your minds up because you have ten seconds before you press one of those buzzers.'

OMG, I thought. We're about to win thirty thousand pounds.

On a large screen behind them, the numbers counted down in big, flashy colours, while tense music played in the background. The audience joined in the countdown.

We could see a close-up of Dad's and Madge's hands hovered over their silver buzzers.

THREE, TWO …

Dad's going to do a last minute switch, I thought.

ONE

The music stopped.

He's gonna switch.

But he didn't. He hit the silver.

Madge, however, hit the gold.

Mum let out a groan.

Danielle shouted, 'No!'

I heard myself gasp, 'What the …'

On screen, the message flashed, 'MADGE WINS IT ALL! DANNY WINS NOTHING!'

The treacherous old biddy was jumping up and down like an excited bunny.

Dad held his head in his hands and he looked all sort of crumpled.

The presenter rubbed his hands together gleefully. 'Well, that's the way the cookie crumbles, folks. In the words of Frank Sinatra, "*That's life*". This is why we call our little show *All or Nothing*.'

He beckoned the two finalists into the centre. 'Well played, Madge, you played a blinder. Commiserations,

Danny. I think you met your match, there.' He waved at the camera. 'See you all next week for another exciting edition of *All or Nothing*.'

As we headed out of the studio, Madge came over, a bit red-faced, and sort of apologised. I muttered a few choice words. Mum hissed at me to be quiet.

'Sorry, luv,' Madge said to my dad. 'I'm not normally like that. I don't know what came over me.'

'Greed,' I muttered. Mum gave me a push.

'But I suppose it was just a game, after all,' said kindly old Madge. 'I've always been good at games.'

Dad nodded tearfully. 'Well done, luv,' he said.

The rest of us couldn't bring ourselves to speak to her.

* * *

The atmosphere was pretty tense and strained on the journey home.

'Sorry everyone,' said Dad. 'I thought I was doing the right thing.'

I stared out of the window at the falling rain.

'I would have done the same thing, luv,' Mum said. I could tell she was gutted, though.

'Well I wouldn't,' I said.

'Nor me,' said Danielle. 'For once I agree with *him*.' She pointed at me.

Dad turned around. 'What was I supposed to do, rob an old lady?'

I shook my head. 'You let yourself get robbed by Gangsta Granny, instead.'

'Richie!' snapped Mum.

Dad faced the road again. 'How was I supposed to know she would do that?' he said, his voice cracking.

'Haven't you seen the show before?' said Danielle. 'People do it every week.'

'And sometimes they both walk away with nothing,' said Mum.

Danielle folded her arms. 'Well, at least lovely old Madge has some money, eh?'

'You should have put *us* first, not her,' I said.

That was a big mistake. I regretted saying it as soon as the words were out of my mouth.

Basically, Mum and Dad laid into us for the rest of the journey, starting with Mum saying, 'How can you say that? We put you first all the time. Ever since you were born, we've put you first ...'

I think we were all in tears by the time we got home. Even the car windows were crying.

*   *   *

I spent the weekend in the house, not daring to leave, occasionally standing by the curtains and peeping outside. There was no sign of my tormentors. The phone went off a few times, but there was no one on the other end.

By Monday, I owed £345.16 and it was mounting up by the second.

Mrs Lloyd didn't help matters by bringing up Children in Need, again. 'Good news and bad news,' she said. 'The good news is that the money has been found in the boys' toilets. The bad news is that the person who took it was probably a boy in the Upper Juniors.'

'Or a teacher,' whispered Owen.

'I would be really disappointed if I thought it was one of you,' said Miss. She sat down on our desk. 'Anyway, as it's nearly time for Children in Need I thought we'd talk about wants and needs.'

There were lots of confused looks.

'Some things we *need*. Other things, we don't actually need them but we might *want* to have them.

'The things we *need* are those things important for us to survive, things we truly can't do without, for example, a roof over our heads, warmth, food, water, clothes, transport. Some of these things are free. Like air. We all need it but we don't have to pay for it. Exercise can be free, too. We all need to stay fit and healthy. Running around doesn't cost anything. Can anybody think of anything that people don't actually need but might want?'

'A TV?' said Andrea.

'What?' gasped Owen. 'I need my telly. I couldn't possibly do without it. How would I survive without *Family Guy* and *South Park*?'

'But you'd still be able to live,' Miss insisted. 'It's not like going without food or water. You'd manage to survive, somehow.'

'Most people have jobs to earn money, so they can pay for the things they need and then, if they've got some left over, buy some of the things that they want. You can't have everything you want, unless you have an unlimited amount of money.'

'Like Simon Cowell?' said Riley.

'Possibly. It's really important to understand the difference between needs and wants so you can spend your money wisely. Just think what would happen if your family spent your entire income on DVDs and computer games one week, with nothing left over for food or to pay your other bills.'

'Is a car a need or a want?' Raj asked.

'Good question. Needs and wants can get a bit tricky. Your mum or dad use a car to drive you to school, get to work, go to the supermarket. In most cases, people *need* a car. But, in many cases, people like to have a car that is bigger or more expensive than what they really need. So, even though a car is a need, the car that many people choose might actually be a want. The extra money spent on the larger or more luxurious car is money that could have been saved or spent on something else.

'Food is another example. We all need nutritious food in order to grow and be healthy. For example, we need to eat protein, fruits and vegetables to get the energy, vitamins and minerals that we need to survive. We also need to drink lots of liquids to stay alive. But do we need ice cream? Do we need Coca-Cola?'

'I do,' said Owen.

We spent the rest of the lesson looking through magazines and catalogues, cutting out pictures and sorting them into needs and wants.

I was very clear about what I needed. I needed and wanted to be safe and warm and not have my legs broken.

CHAPTER EIGHT

Being Rich

I had to make my way home on my own that evening. Owen had left early to go to the dentist.

Halfway to my destination, I spotted trouble ahead. The very people I was trying to avoid. They were in the process of wrecking a bus stop. I took a quick detour, moving swiftly, my feet hardly touching the ground.

By tomorrow, I would owe them £379.67. More than the price of a PS4 on e-Bay.

I had a plan. It was a horrible plan, low down and dirty. You would have thought I'd learned my lesson by now. If God was watching, he definitely wouldn't be impressed. But, as far as I was concerned, all of my options had run out.

My nan – Nana Price – lives about half a mile away from us. She's not really my nan, she's my dad's nan.

She's eighty-five and lives on her own, in a ground-floor flat on the other side of the estate.

This is the important bit. My dad has said, quite a few times, that Nana Price doesn't trust banks and keeps her money under her mattress.

I wasn't 100% sure if this was true, but why would he say it if it wasn't?

I was thinking that maybe I could borrow some of it, without her noticing. I'd pay it back, of course, when I'd saved up enough pocket money.

This was money to keep me alive.

After tea, I informed Mum and Dad that I was going to call for Owen. I pulled my bike out of the shed and wheeled it around the side of the house, peeking around the corner to make sure it was all clear.

I had the most nerve-wracking journey of my life as I weaved my way through the estate. I half-expected Riley's brother voice to call after me at any moment, or one of his mates to pop up from behind a hedge like a rabid bulldog. I avoided going anywhere near the shopping centre.

Nana Price lives in a lime-green three-storey block

of flats. I chained the bike to the stairwell inside the building.

She took ages answering the door, and only opened it a crack.

'Who is it?' she called out

'It's me, Rich.'

'Who?'

'Me, Richie, your great-grandson.'

I don't visit her very often.

She unlocked about fifty chains. It was like Fort Knox. Burglars would never get in there.

'Well, what a nice surprise,' she beamed. 'Come on in, luv.'

Her flat smells a bit funny, a bit flowery and a bit fousty. Sort of an old-person smell. It's a tiny flat. There's a living room, a kitchen, a bathroom and a bedroom, that's all. The rooms are cluttered with ornaments and knick-knacks and trinkets. The wallpaper and furniture are well out of date. There's a painting over the fireplace of sunlight bursting through stormy clouds.

I spotted her Bible, which has a black leather cover, next to her empty breakfast dish.

She led me to the sofa. 'Sit down,' she said. 'Did

you have a good birthday? I hope you got my envelope with the money in it. I knew you'd rather have the money than a present.'

At the mention of the word money, my heart went pitter-pat.

I leant over and gave her a peck on the cheek. 'Yeah, thanks Nan.'

We had a bit of a chat. Basically, she chatted and I listened: about Mrs So-and-So in the upstairs flat whose dog got run over last week, about Mrs Jones's sister-in-law's niece who lives down the road and who recently had an eye operation …

This went on for a good twenty minutes.

She patted me on the knee. 'What am I thinking? You must be starving. Fancy a cup of tea? And a Cherry Bakewell?'

I hate Cherry Bakewells. 'Yes thanks, Nan,' I said. 'Do you mind if I use the toilet?'

She stood up. 'As long as you don't mind looking at my wet clothes hanging over the bath.'

I didn't even want to think about that.

Nan's bathroom is right next to her bedroom. The doors are virtually touching each other.

She headed off to the kitchen while I loped off in the opposite direction.

I closed the living room door behind me and opened her bedroom door. Her curtains were slightly open, allowing a shaft of sunlight to break through.

Her bedroom smelled exactly like the living room. Bible pictures hung everywhere. I felt like God was watching me from every angle.

But Riley's brother was watching me too, and that little devil on my shoulder was reminding me about buses and broken legs. I'd never had a broken bone before. It couldn't be much fun.

I bent down and lifted the corner of her mattress. It was incredibly heavy. There was nothing under there except wooden slats. I checked the pillows. Nothing.

So, it was a joke, after all. There was no money.

My foot kicked against something.

I knelt down. An old blue suitcase lay under the bed. I dragged it out. The little key was still in the case.

I glanced briefly at Jesus's face above the headboard, then turned the key and flipped the case open.

Inside were some ancient-looking baby clothes,

Bible books and photos. There was one of Nana Price when she was a lot younger, with her husband Jack, in his policeman's uniform. He looked like a tough guy. He wouldn't be very happy with me right now.

I noticed an Asda carrier bag near the bottom of the case. I prodded it. More photos?

I opened the neck of the bag and peeped inside. And there it was. Loads of it. Fives, tens and twenties, none of it bundled together, all loose. I had no idea how much was in there, but it was a lot.

'Are you alright, luv?' Nana Price called out.

It was now or never. I could easily scoop up two hundred or so in a matter of seconds. She probably wouldn't notice it was gone for months. I would save up and pay it back.

I glanced from Jesus to the Virgin Mary to the photo of Grandpa Jack and back to Jesus again. Then I stared at all that money. My heart felt like it was tap-dancing.

There was a sudden loud bang on the window behind me.

I froze.

Afraid to turn around, I just casually closed the case and pushed it back under. Scooting into the bathroom, I quickly pulled the flush, then strolled into the living room, trying to appear calm and relaxed, just as my dad walked in. He glared at me.

'Ooh, look,' said Nana Price excitedly, 'two gentleman callers in one day. Aren't I the lucky one?'

Dad forced a smile. 'I've come to look at your leaky tap, Nan,' he said.

'Ooh I forgot,' she said, struggling to get up. 'I'll show you.' She made her way to the kitchen.

Dad hissed at me as she walked past. 'Sit there and drink your tea, you. You've got some explaining to do. Enjoy your Cherry Bakewell.'

I couldn't sit still as Nana Price talked at me and fussed over me while my dad worked on the leak. She kept asking me if I was okay.

I wasn't.

*　　*　　*

Dad made me sit in the car with him. Above us, dark clouds were rolling in.

'Well?' he said.

'Well, what?' I planned to tough it out.

'What were you doing?'

'When?'

Dad bit his lower lip. 'Back there, in the bedroom.'

'I wasn't in the bedroom. I went to the loo.'

He turned to face me. 'I saw you, Richie, kneeling down by the bed, where Nana keeps her money. I'm not stupid.'

Oh God. I was finding it hard to breathe.

'I wanted to see if it was true. That she had money under the bed.'

He grabbed my arm. 'If I thought you were lying to me …'

'I'm not.'

'Look, there's something really fishy going on here and I don't like it one bit.'

I was silent.

Dad shook his head in disgust. 'You better get on your bike and go home. It's gonna rain any second.'

I was so preoccupied with what had just happened that I forgot to take the shortcut home and ended up riding past the shopping centre.

Neil Jones and his gang were loitering outside the library on the other side of the road from me.

They spotted me straight away. 'Oy, oy!' one called out. Breaking into a sprint, they headed after me.

I raised my bum off the saddle and pedalled for my life.

Dad was just getting out of his car as I pulled up, the rampaging hordes behind me.

He folded his arms and faced them. 'You lot again.'

'He's got my money!' Neil yelled, trying to barge his way past.

Dad spun around and looked at me. 'What's he talking about?'

I said nothing.

'Right,' he said, grabbing me by the sleeve, 'you and me are going to have a serious talk.'

'I want my MONEY!' Neil yelled, swaggering around like a chimpanzee.

Dad pulled me inside. The house was empty, apart from us. Mum and Danielle had gone shopping.

We sat at the dinner table, face-to-face. 'You're not leaving this room until I've found out what's going on,' he said.

Outside, Neil was still ranting and raving.

'You *do* have his money, don't you? This is all about money, isn't it?'

My knuckles were white.

'Richie?'

There was no way out of this.

Dad stood up, then sat down next to me. He put his hand on my shoulder. 'Look, you can tell me anything. Whatever you've done, we can sort it. That's what dads are for.'

A warm tear rolled down my cheek.

'But I'm ashamed.'

'Okay. But we all make mistakes. I promise you, whatever it is, I forgive you. As long as you haven't murdered anyone.' He paused. 'You haven't, have you?'

I smiled through my tears.

And then I told him what I'd done. I told about borrowing the hundred pounds.

He frowned in disbelief.

What I didn't tell him was about the money from school that I'd nearly stolen. However, I think he was clever enough to work out that I had actually intended to take some of Nana Price's money.

I said sorry and broke down.

Dad shook his head. 'This is all about your birthday, isn't it? It's my fault. I wish we could have got you more. I did try to explain. Money's really tight at the moment. I'm not even sure my job is secure.' He passed me some tissues.

I heard a bin being kicked over outside.

'Have you got the hundred to pay him back?'

'It's not a hundred any more.'

'What do you mean?'

'He charges interest. As of today, it's £345.16.'

Dad was open-mouthed. 'What? The little thug. Well, the police will be very interested in what he's up to.'

'Please don't call the police,' I pleaded.

He frowned. 'I'm sorting this, right now.'

He got his phone out of his pocket.

'Who are you ringing?' I asked nervously.

'Your Uncle Frank.' He disappeared into the hallway.

Uncle Frank is ex-army and a bouncer. He weighs about eighteen stone. Everyone's scared of him, including me.

I checked outside. My tormentors had gone.

A minute later, Dad came back in. 'Me and your Uncle Frank are going to pay the Jones family a visit. Lock the door after me.'

* * *

I sat there and stewed in my own shame and guilt. What had I been thinking?

If I needed money in future, I was going to earn it. Selling lemonade with Raj, washing cars, doing a paper round. Whatever it took.

A half-hour later, Dad returned, a bit red-faced. 'Right,' he said. 'It's sorted.'

'What do you mean?'

'Debt paid. No interest. No comebacks.'

'Really?'

'Really. Your Uncle Frank can be very persuasive. You've got to promise to stay away from those boys. Choose your friends carefully.'

'They're definitely not my friends,' I said.

Dad gave me a hug. 'I hope you've learned your lesson.'

He didn't have to worry about that.

* * *

It was the Friday before half-term and we spent the morning presenting our homework. I thought it might all be pretty boring, but it turned out not to be. Everybody had come at the money topic from a slightly different angle.

Logan Johnson, who is a Maths whizz-kid, used Excel to show us various graphs and pie charts about the pocket money of kids in Wales. Apparently, the average 5 to 8-year-old gets £2.62, the average 9 to 11-year-old gets £3.82 and the average 12 to 15-year-old gets £6.96. I was amazed that 5 to 8 year-olds were actually given pocket money.

Owen did his five-minute stand-up routine on the theme of money. It was pretty funny even if most of the jokes were old.

This was part of his act:

I said to my nan the other day, 'Nan, your legs look like they're worth a million dollars.' 'Do they?' she beamed. 'Yeah,' I said, 'all green and crinkly.'

I asked my mum for a new bike. She said, 'I'm not made of money, y'know'. I said, 'Oh yes you are. M-O-M. Made-Of-Money.'

Why did the robber take a bath before he stole from the bank? So he could make a clean getaway.

Did you know that the singer 50 Cent has a half-brother? He's called 25 Cent.

He finished with a knock-knock joke.

Knock knock. Who's there? Cash. Cash who? I always knew you were a nut.

They weren't particularly new or good jokes but, when he's on form, Owen can read out the phone book and make it sound like the funniest thing ever.

Riley had found out the names of money or currency used in lots of different countries. In India they use the rupee, in South Africa they use the rand. In Poland they use zloty. In Malaysia they have ringgits. In Mozambique they use meticals. In Vietnam they have dong. In Thailand they use bahts, but it's pronounced butts. You can buy a hat for fifteen bahts.

Andrea had created quite a moving PowerPoint about charity. She informed everyone that Muslims give 2.5% of their income to charity and that, if we all did this, there would be no more poverty in the world. She encouraged us all to help out in the upcoming Children in Need. Last year, she told us, £7 billion was donated to charity by individuals in the UK. That breaks down to an average annual donation of £150 per person. Two-thirds of givers donate up to £5 in a typical month. A small number of 'elite' givers donate upwards of £50 a month. 16 million people donate nothing to charity. Some people donate their time rather than money, which is just as important.

Raj showed us his business plan, his marketing strategies and his bookkeeping skills. To be fair he had worked hard, and he brought us some lemonade to sample for free. He was giving 50% of his profits to charity. I'd completely misjudged him. One thing I've learned is that you can't blame someone for having parents who are better off than yours.

Mrs Lloyd left me until last. I think she suspected that I hadn't done anything. But I had. I'd written a short, personal speech. It wasn't a confession. I'm not that brave.

I called my speech, 'Being Rich.' My dad helped me a bit with it. This is a little part of it:

My name, as you know, is Rich, but I've never really known what it means to be rich.

I've learned a lot about money over the last few weeks, about bartering, about wages and salaries, goods and services, wants, needs and choices, but I've also learned this:

Some people think that money is everything. Other people think that it's not important at all.

I've learned that money shouldn't be important

at all but, because of the kind of world we live in, it is. It's still not as important as some people think it is, though. Generally, if you work hard and you live in a certain part of the world, then you can enjoy a comfortable life with enough money for a nice house, car, clothes, holidays, hobbies.

Some people make a lot of money and they keep wanting more and more of it, competing with others. To them, money becomes more important than living. It becomes like a god to them.

In my opinion, the whole point about having money is that it allows you to do things with your friends and with your family.

Ultimately, your family and friends and your good health are more important than money.

And it is possible to be rich without having a lot of money, if you're surrounded by people you love.

My dad says that happiness is not about getting what you want, it's about appreciating what you have.

Andrea smiled at me. My face was on fire.

I am rich. I may not have the best clothes, I may not go to the best places on holiday, or even have a flash car, but I do have a mum and dad who love me, a roof over my head, food in my belly and good friends.

There are lots of children in the world who don't have what we have in Wales and the UK, which is why we have things like Comic Relief and Children in Need. Hopefully, I've learned to be more grateful for what I've got. I'm going to definitely try and stop constantly whingeing about things that I want.

I finished with: *My name is Rich, but I've never really known what it means to be rich – until now.*

Miss nodded her head a few times and gave me a clap. 'Wow, thanks, Richie. I wasn't expecting that. What a great way to finish our project on money. Well done, everyone. You all did fantastically well.'

'What are we doing next term?' Owen asked.

Mrs Lloyd shook her head. 'I haven't made my mind up yet. Perhaps you can all help me.'

'I fancy doing dinosaurs,' said Owen.

'We'll see,' she smiled. 'Anyway, everyone give yourself a pat on the back. You've all done a great job.'

* * *

You won't believe what happened next, especially when you consider all the lessons I'd just learned.

When I got home, Dad was on the phone, looking

ever so slightly confused. 'Are you serious?' he said. I thought for one second he was angry. 'But why?' he said. 'I see … I see … Well, I don't know what to say. Thank you very much.' He put the phone back in his pocket.

Mum came in from the kitchen, a damp tea towel in her hand. 'Who was that?'

'Madge.'

'Madge who?'

'Gangsta Granny,' I explained.

'Oh, what does she want?'

Dad sat down. 'Well, it turns out she's not so gangsta after all.'

'What do you mean?'

Mum and I both sat down too.

Dad shook his head. 'She says she's been feeling guilty about her decision to hit the gold button. She's had second thoughts, discussed it with her children and decided to give us some of the prize money.'

My eyes widened. 'How much?'

Dad smiled. 'Half of it.'

I jumped out of my seat. 'Woo-hoo!! Fifteen thousand pounds! Fifteen thousand pounds!'

Granddad and Danielle came downstairs to see what all the fuss was about.

'Can we have a share?' Danielle asked.

Dad thought about it. 'Let me think. I want us to have a good holiday, there's the boiler … and we need a new car. You can probably have five hundred pounds each.'

Granddad pointed a finger at me. 'Don't forget you owe me a tenner.'

Dad gave me a bit of a frown.

'Is it okay if I give some to charity?' I said.

'Of course,' said Mum. 'It's your money. I might give some too.'

'Who said *you're* getting a share,' Dad laughed.

I used a calculator to work out 2.5% of £500. It was £12.50. That didn't seem enough so I doubled it. I would donate £25 to Children in Need.

I decided I would buy tickets for me, Owen and Andrea to go and see Wales v Australia at the Principality Stadium. I'd never been to an International before and nor had they.

I'd have a think about what to do with the rest of the money. Meanwhile, I'd set up a bank savings account. I certainly wasn't going to keep my money under the bed.

*   *   *

You may be interested to know that I am now the not-so-proud owner of a PS4.

I didn't buy it.

Father Christmas brought it for me.

Looks like I was meant to have one, even though I'm pretty sure I didn't deserve it.

There must have been some sort of mix-up on the Naughty or Nice list.

Next year, I'm definitely going to make sure I'm on the Nice list to make up for it.

≈

Paul Manship was born in Newport and, aside from a short spell in South Africa as a child, has lived there all of his life.

He has been a primary school teacher for nearly thirty years. His pupils inspired him to write.

Kerching! is Paul's sixth publication. He won the Tir na n-Og in 2010 for 'Dear Mr Author'.

Paul loves reading horror, thrillers and autobiographies. He is a cinema buff and enjoys listening to film soundtracks.

Paul lives in Rhiwderin with his wife Derryn. He has three daughters, Olivia, Rosie and Alice. He often writes about underdogs and children who have to fight against the odds.